CIRIA C567

Working with wildlife site guide

J Newton Ecology Consultancy Ltd

C Thackray Ecology Consultancy Ltd

B Nicholson Ecology Consultancy Ltd

CIRIA *sharing knowledge* ■ *building best practice*

Classic House, 174-180 Old Street, London, EC1V 9BP
Telephone: 020 7549 3300   Fax: 020 7253 0523
Email: enquiries@ciria.org   Website: www.ciria.org

Summary

This guide presents information and guidance to enable a wide range of people working in, with or for the construction industry to stay within the law relating to wildlife, and to understand and implement good practice in relation to wildlife on development and construction projects. It provides an introduction to legislation governing wildlife and construction issues, practical guidance on dealing with wildlife on sites, references and contact details where further guidance can be obtained, and materials on individual species and different types of habitats.

It is intended for use as a guide principally for those working at the construction site level but it provides information that will be helpful for all those involved in the construction process.

Working with wildlife site guide

Lead author: John Newton

CIRIA C567   © 2005   ISBN 0-86017-567-7

Keywords		
biodiversity, environmental good practice, site management, sustainable construction		

Reader interest	Classification	
Contractors, environmental managers, ecologists	AVAILABILITY CONTENT	Unrestricted Guidance
	STATUS USER	Committee-guided Contractors, environmental managers, ecologists

Published by CIRIA, Classic House, 174-180 Old Street, London EC1V 9BP

Acknowledgements

Authors

John Newton BSc MSc MIEEM
John Newton is managing director of Ecology Consultancy Ltd and environment director of Crane Environmental Ltd. An ecologist with more than 30 years experience, including work in the voluntary and private sectors, he has spent the last 15 years actively involved in working with the construction industry to improve its performance on ecological issues.

Dr Clair Thackray BSc PhD
Clair Thackray (nee Williams) is an ecologist with Ecology Consultancy Ltd and a specialist on great crested newts and protected species. She is currently carrying out site assessments and devising mitigation strategies for great crested newts and other protected species on development sites around the country.

Barry Nicholson BSc MSc MIEEM
Barry Nicholson is principal ecologist with Ecology Consultancy Ltd. He has more than 25 years experience as an ecologist working in the voluntary, public and private sectors. He has worked as an ecologist on a number of major construction projects including several Channel Tunnel Rail Link contracts.

Steering group

Rod Dengate (Chair)	Skanska Construction
Angus Corby	Scottish Executive
Keith Davies	Countryside Council for Wales
Helen Doran	English Nature
David Farebrother	Land Securities
Gemma Fenn	Carillion Infrastructure Management
Alex Hazel	Environment Agency
Mervyn Jones	Davis Langdon and Everest
Alan McKirdy	Scottish Natural Heritage
Mike Oxford	Association of Local Government Ecologists
Mark Southgate	RSPB
Jørgen Schouten	URS Corporation Ltd (initially at Bovis Lend Lease)
Gregor Watson	Environment and Heritage Service, NI
Len Wyatt	Welsh Assembly Government.

CIRIA's research manager for the project was Martin Hunt.

Project

When CIRIA published the *Working with wildlife resource training pack* (C587) in 2004, it soon became clear that there was an opportunity to develop a site guide about wildlife on construction sites. *Working with wildlife site guide* has been developed from the training pack, and updated with new information for practical application by those working on site.

Contributors

CIRIA gratefully acknowledges the support of the funding organisations and the technical advice and help provided by members of the steering group. The authors would also like to express special thanks to: The Bat Conservation Trust, Julie Brownbridge, Dr Mairi Cole (SNH), Rachel Cook (EN), Elizabeth Cryer (SEERAD), the Environment Agency, Environment and Heritage Services (NI), Fisheries Research Services Freshwater Laboratory, Tony Gent (HCT), Peter Harvey, Tony Hutson, Claire Hyland, Elaine King (NFBG), Penny Lewns, Jim Walker (EA), Kevin Morgan, National Federation of Badger Groups, Mike Oxford, Carys Roberts (CCW), Graham Scholey (EA, Wallingford), Jørgen Schouten, (URS Corp), Rob Strachan, Paul Chanin, Michael Woods (Scottish Environmental Protection Agency), Mark Southgate (RSPB), Huw Thomas, Graeme Waugh and Len Wyatt.

Photographs were provided by: Hugh Clark, Cresswell Associates, English Nature (photographers: Paul Glendell, Peter Roworth, Peter Wakely), Jim Lawrence, John Newton, Barry Nicholson, Mike Oxford, RSPB-Images.com (photographers: Steve Austin, Chris Gomesall, George McCarthy, Richard Revels, Roger Wilmshurst), Jørgen Schouten, Skanska Construction, Hugh Venables, Roger Venables.

Publication editor John Tomlin

Working with wildlife. Resource and training pack for the construction industry. CIRIA publication: C587.

This attractive, highly-illustrated mixed media pack presents information and guidance for a wide range of people in construction to stay within the law relating to wildlife, and implement good practice in protecting wildlife on development and construction projects.

The pack is presented in a sturdy ring-binder, and all the presentation and training materials are included in an accompanying CD-Rom. The pack can be used either for individual study or support, or as a resource for anyone setting up a wildlife training event.

Full details can be found on the CIRIA online bookshop: **www.ciriabooks.com**

Contents

Glossary

compensation   Measures taken to offset significant residual impacts, ie those that cannot be entirely avoided or mitigated to the point that they become insignificant.

conservation   A series of measures required to maintain or restore natural habitats and populations of species of wild fauna and flora.

disturbance   Disruption of natural process or behaviour.

ecology   The scientific study of the inter-relationship among and between organisms, and between them and all aspects, living and non-living, of their environment.

enhancement   To increase value and importance for wildlife.

environmental impact assessment (EIA)   Procedure for ensuring that the likely effects of a new development on the environment are fully understood and taken into account before it is allowed to go ahead.

habitat   The place where an organism lives, often defined on the basis of uniformity of vegetation (woodland, reedbed etc).

mitigation   Measures taken to reduce adverse impacts.

Phase 1 survey   A standardised system for identifying and mapping habitats. (NB: Phase 1 is also used in other forms of environmental audit to mean different things).

population   A group comprising the same species present in the same locality.

protected species   Certain plant or animal species that are protected to various degrees in law, particularly by the Wildlife and Countryside Act 1981 (as amended).

species   A group of organisms that resemble each other closely and can interbreed within the group but cannot exchange genes with other groups.

translocation   The physical removal of either an area of habitat or a number of individuals of a certain species from one site (the donor site) to another (the receptor site).

watching brief   The process by which a person (usually an ecologist) oversees construction activity and works to ensure that they comply with wildlife legislation, good practice and any previously agreed method statements or conditions.

Abbreviations

AONB   Area of Outstanding Natural Beauty

ASSI   Area of Special Scientific Interest (Northern Ireland)

BAP   Biodiversity Action Plan

CCW   Countryside Council for Wales (SNCO for Wales)

CWS   Countryside Wildlife Site

DARD   Department of Agriculture and Rural Development (Northern Ireland)

Defra   Department for Environment, Food and Rural Affairs

EA   Environment Agency

EHS-EP (NI)   Environment and Heritage Service – Environmental Protection (Northern Ireland)

EHS-NH (NI)   Environment and Heritage Service – Natural Heritage (SNCO for Northern Ireland)

EIA   environmental impact assessment

EMS   environmental management system

EN   English Nature (SNCO for England)

LNR   Local Nature Reserve

LPA   local planning authority *(normally the county or borough council in a particular area – or region in Scotland)*

MNR   Marine Nature Reserve

MPG   mineral planning guidance notes

NNR   National Nature Reserve

NPPG	national planning policy guidance (in Scotland)
PAN	planning advice note (in Wales)
PPG	planning policy guidance
PPS	planning policy statement
RSPB	Royal Society for the Protection of Birds
SAC	Special Area of Conservation
cSAC	candidate Special Area of Conservation
SEPA	Scottish Environment Protection Agency
SEERAD	Scottish Executive Environment and Rural Affairs Department
SINC	Site of Importance for Nature Conservation
SNCI	Site of Nature Conservation Importance
SNCO	Statutory Nature Conservation Organisation (ie EN, CCW, EHS-NH(NI), SNH)
SNH	Scottish Natural Heritage (SNCO for Scotland)
SPA	Special Protection Area
SSSI	Site of Special Scientific Interest
TAN	technical advice note (in Wales)
WA	Welsh Assembly
WHS	Wildlife Heritage Site.

Introduction to this guide

The aim of this site guide is to help those involved in the construction industry to move from a situation of doing little for wildlife to one where good practice is implemented on every project to everyone's benefit. It is not about just complying with the law nor, indeed, about going beyond compliance, but it is about how value can be added to a project by adopting best practice, to ensure people and wildlife both come out as winners.

Principally the guide is aimed at contractors. However, it is hoped that it will also appeal to a variety of environmental professionals. It is designed to cover all sorts of projects – large and small, rural and urban, upland and lowland, coastal and inland, housing, civil engineering, infrastructure, flood defence, building construction, extraction and landfill – and cover such work in all parts of the UK. Wildlife occurs everywhere and, generally, the principles of dealing with it are the same wherever it is found, even though the details may vary.

A toolbox talk held from a van especially adapted for the purpose.

Overview of how construction can affect wildlife

HOW DEVELOPMENT AND CONSTRUCTION CAN IMPACT ON ECOLOGY

Most development sites will have some wildlife interest, whether they are situated in rural or urban areas. The most important wildlife sites are usually designated in some way although other sites may still have wildlife interest, but are not designated or otherwise protected. Obviously, the more important a place is for wildlife – or if it contains legally protected species – the more care will have to be taken during the development process. In general, wherever there is some wildlife value on a site, this should be acknowledged and the potential adverse impacts on it avoided, if possible, or reduced to a minimum if not.

Badgers can turn up unexpectedly on construction sites – although not usually in daylight!

The loss of lots of small areas of wildlife, which may not appear all that significant if taken alone, can have a significant effect when taken together and can jeopardise the survival of wildlife associated with the more important sites in the same area and beyond.

The construction industry may affect wildlife in a number of different ways.

Direct habitat and species loss – the development of a site may mean that an area of wildlife habitat is lost. That habitat will support various plants and animals, and so these also will be lost. Where habitats and species have been identified as being particularly important, special measures may need to be taken, either to avoid or minimise the loss or to mitigate for it during the construction process. Habitat loss may not always be obvious, for example replacement of a roof may result in the loss of valuable habitat for nesting birds such as swifts or house martins, or roosting bats.

Fragmentation – fragmentation of habitats is almost as bad for wildlife as direct habitat loss. Fragmentation is when an area of habitat is split into two or more parts, usually with a different type of land use between the parts. In terms of

construction, linear projects are often responsible for fragmentation of habitats. A road, railway or pipeline passing through a wood, for example, not only results in the direct loss of habitat, but the fragmentation of the remaining parts.

Fragmentation of habitats still results in fewer species, even when the total amount of habitat is the same as it was originally. In addition, animals may still try to cross between the two areas of habitat – if a road or a railway is between, this can result in animal deaths.

Linear projects such as roads and railway lines create a barrier dividing existing habitats and causing fragmentation.

Disturbance – disturbance due to the increased human presence, or from noise pollution, may have a detrimental affect on animals, preventing them from breeding successfully or from feeding in the area. This may lead to their temporary or permanent loss from the site. Ensure that the most sensitive areas of the site are known and recognised by all staff and, where possible, ensure that potentially disturbing activities are kept well clear of such areas – especially during the breeding season. It is an offence to disturb some species of animals when they are breeding, for example Schedule 1 birds (See page 65).

Other types of disturbance include altering the structure of soil by compaction and adversely affecting the hydrology of a site, resulting in the loss of species and changes in habitat type.

Having Japanese knotweed on a site can lead to unintentionally spreading the plant unless preventative measures are taken.

Types of damage or loss – some wildlife loss or damage associated with construction may be **permanent, temporary** or **direct,** for example the loss of a tree with a bird's nest in it. Others may be indirect, for example the pollution of a water course that results in the loss of fish spawning habitat downstream. When planning and designing a construction project, avoid permanent impacts if at all possible and consider indirect as well as direct impacts.

Peat bogs take thousands of years to develop. Once destroyed, for instance to gain peat compost for gardening, they are irretrievably lost.

When considering indirect impacts, don't forget the **supply chain!** Materials, products and services, and the way they have been sourced and procured, may have a dramatic effect on wildlife resources elsewhere in the UK or abroad – for example the purchase of timber if it has not been sourced from a sustainably managed forest. The use of peat as a soil improver in landscape design has resulted in the loss of some of Britain's most important wildlife sites.

Introducing pest species or causing them to spread – feral pigeons, rats, and plants such as Japanese knotweed, can pose problems to a development if not handled in the right way. Carrying out good practice and keeping within the law in dealing with these species are important.

Construction activities and their potential adverse effects on wildlife

Construction activity	Implication	Examples of effect on wildlife
Site clearance	Removal of tree and shrubs	<ul><li>loss of important species or specimens of tree or shrub that may be protected by a TPO</li><li>loss of bird nests or bat roosts</li><li>loss of habitat for protected species</li><li>loss of important invertebrates, including those that may require deadwood habitat (eg stag beetles)</li></ul>
	Removal of ground vegetation	<ul><li>loss of habitat for protected species</li><li>loss of rare plants</li><li>loss of bird nests</li><li>killing or injury of reptiles or amphibians</li><li>killing or injury of small mammals</li><li>loss of invertebrates and their breeding habitat</li></ul>
	Removal of soil	<ul><li>loss of habitat for protected species</li><li>loss of seed bank</li><li>loss of water vole burrows</li><li>loss of invertebrates and their breeding habitat</li><li>destruction of badger setts</li></ul>
	Demolition of buildings and structures	<ul><li>loss of bird nesting or bat roosting areas</li></ul>
	Removal of rubble and other materials	<ul><li>loss of reptile and amphibian habitat</li></ul>
Site setup	Location of site offices and compounds	<ul><li>disturbance of breeding animals</li></ul>
	Storage area	<ul><li>potential for pollution of important watercourses, wetlands or other waterbodies, including coastal waters, through spillage or dust</li></ul>
Establishment of haul roads	Rubble or concrete temporary roads constructed	<ul><li>fragmentation of habitats</li><li>road kills</li><li>destruction of badger setts</li><li>contamination of adjoining habitats by dust</li><li>noise or light pollution may disturb nesting birds or other animals</li><li>change of soil pH through leaching</li></ul>
Groundworks	Ground investigations Foundations Excavations and piling Temporary earthworks Tunnelling	<ul><li>impacts on surface- and groundwater, which may have secondary impacts on important wetlands both on and off site</li><li>noise or light pollution may disturb nesting birds or other animals</li><li>destruction of badger setts</li><li>run-off and erosion, which may damage important habitats</li><li>potential to introduce or spread invasive plants such as Japanese knotweed</li></ul>
Construction	Concrete pours and other wet trades	<ul><li>contamination of wetlands</li><li>change of soil pH through run-off</li></ul>

WHAT CAN THE CONSTRUCTION INDUSTRY DO TO MAXIMISE OPPORTUNITIES FOR ECOLOGICAL ENHANCEMENT AND TO MINIMISE ADVERSE IMPACTS?

With careful planning, and by working closely with a site ecologist, construction projects can offer numerous opportunities to enhance the wildlife value of a site, as explained below.

The first maxim for the industry in this respect has to be: **know your site and your wildlife.** So, find out:

- whether the site, or any areas adjoining it, are designated as being of importance for wildlife in any way

- whether it contains protected species of animal or plant

- and, even if the whole site is not designated, are there any parts of the site of particular importance for wildlife that may constrain or even prevent development?

If any of these apply to a site being considered for purchase, then it may be wise to consider alternative locations.

Once a site has been acquired and what is to be done with it has been decided, make sure that its ecology, and any special interest in this respect, is known and understood.

ECOLOGICAL SURVEY – WHAT SHOULD HAVE BEEN DONE IN THE EARLY STAGES

The content and duration of an ecological survey will depend, to a large extent, on the nature of the site – normally a broad habitat survey will be carried out as a starting point. These are called **Phase 1 Habitat Surveys** and follow a format laid down by the Joint Nature Conservation Committee.

Depending on what was found out about the site, a Phase 1 survey may then be followed by more detailed Phase 2 surveys of specific groups of plants and animals. The timing of these surveys is critical. Many plants and animals are just not evident at certain times of year – carrying out surveys at inappropriate times will be of very limited use in judging the interest of a site.

Be aware, therefore, that detailed surveys – especially of protected species – may take months to complete.
A survey programme of 12 months or more may be necessary in some cases.

Detailed surveys (left) – especially of protected species – may take months to complete.

SURVEYING AND PROTECTED SPECIES

It is essential that protected species are considered at the very earliest stages of the development process. Planning guidance across the UK makes it clear that nature conservation should be a *material consideration* in determining any planning application. In compliance with this, SNCOs advise that surveys should be undertaken before planning permission is sought, so that development is designed to avoid any impacts on protected species.

Leaving surveys until a later stage increases the risk that plans for the development will have to be redesigned or halted (temporarily or permanently) if protected species are found. In such cases works will have to wait until surveys and any mitigation have been completed and any necessary licences obtained. This process can be very complex, time-consuming and usually can be conducted only at specific times of year. In most cases time delays will last several weeks or months. (See surveys and mitigation table).

ASSESSING AND AVOIDING NEGATIVE IMPACTS

Avoid negative impacts on ecology wherever possible. Where important habitats or species have been identified on a site, design the development and carry out the construction process to avoid destroying or disturbing these wherever possible.

Where disturbance or destruction of habitats is unavoidable ensure that there is sufficient mitigation or compensation within the development at least to retain or replace some of the interest either on site or within the local area. Much of this will be guided by, sometimes prescriptive, legal requirements and accepted good practice.

Wherever possible, mitigation and compensation should be undertaken on-site. Remember the hierarchy:

Avoid	Case study: *Thomas Lawrence Brickworks, Bracknell*
<ul><li>designated or other sites of recognised wildlife importance</li><li>important wildlife habitats on site or those that act as a buffer area for adjacent wildlife areas</li><li>fragmenting existing areas of habitat</li></ul>	A 12 ha site, which is partly a Wildlife Heritage site and partly landfill, was proposed for a new residential development of up to 190 houses and open space. On receipt of the planning application, the council's ecologist surveyed the site and found great crested newt eggs in a pond. The applicant agreed to:<ul><li>remove a 1 acre area from the development to provide a GCN reserve</li><li>move the proposed location of the open space so that it would retain those parts of the Wildlife Heritage site that were considered to offer the best prospects for retention in their current form.</li></ul>

Mitigation

- reduce the impact by utilising less-damaging designs or working methods
- move the affected habitat or species to another part of the site (or in extreme circumstances off-site) – often called translocation.

Compensation

- re-create habitat that has been lost – together with nesting, roosting or resting places – on another part of the site (or in extreme circumstances off-site).

Be aware that mitigation and compensation can be both difficult and expensive. In many cases it is difficult to be sure that such measures will mitigate fully for the loss of any wildlife features. Translocation projects in particular frequently fail. Even where such measures are considered to be successful they may take many years before the full wildlife benefits materialise.

A hibernaculum for great crested newts can be created from construction debris and will provide refuge and habitat for these and other amphibians.

Enhancement

- wherever possible, always endeavour to increase the amount and/or quality of wildlife on site to be more than that which was present before your project began, even if there are no significant adverse impacts of development
- at this point consider opportunities for enhancing wildlife interest particularly regarding BAP species and habitats.

REVIEW OPPORTUNITIES

Once you have a better understanding of the wildlife interest of your proposed construction site you, or your ecologist, will be able to assess the likely impacts on ecology and what can be done to maximise opportunities for enhancement and avoid or minimise any adverse impacts.

Can you carry out any habitat creation on site or is there a possibility for

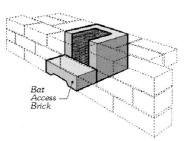

Bat Access Brick

enhancement through more appropriate management of existing habitat? Habitat creation could include, for example, a new pond, areas of woodland or scrub, or a wildflower meadow. Animals such as birds, bats and dormice can be helped by erecting special nesting boxes. Special bird and bat bricks can be built into the walls and roofs of buildings and other structures such as bridges or culverts.

Ecology and construction – what you should do

You should:

- find out about the wildlife interest of your site as early as possible in the development process

- if possible, seek to enhance the wildlife interest of the site whether or not there is any damage or loss

- if there is a potential impact on wildlife resources, avoid it where possible, or mitigate for it and if necessary compensate for any damage or loss

- consider what can be done to buildings and structures to make them more valuable for wildlife

- in cases where on-site compensation is not possible, look at what can be done close by.

Dormouse box

> **Case study:** *Orton brick pits Peterborough*
>
> "The largest colony of great crested newts in Great Britain" was revealed by an environmental impact assessment of the 400 acre development site in 1991.
>
> A subsequent newt survey estimated a population of about 30 000 individuals, which is one tenth of Britain's total GCN population and the biggest known colony in Europe. The site was designated an SSSI in 1995, although it had been granted planning permission in 1993.
>
> The cost of the newt translocation was estimated at £3 m and was paid by the developers. New ponds and habitat were created for them in an 290 acre receptor site.

SCALE AND LOCATION

The larger a site, the more potential there will be for destroying or damaging wildlife, and also for enhancing existing or creating new habitats. Conversely, for more intensive development, off-site compensation may be the only alternative.

Rural sites, especially those dominated by arable agriculture, may not always be very important for wildlife, but development of some sort can help make them more interesting and better managed.

On the other hand, urban wasteland sites are fast disappearing. These often represent some of the most important areas for wildlife and yet they are also prime development sites. The opportunities for mitigation or enhancement in a conventional sense are restricted, if not impossible. However, more and more interest is being shown in the creation of "green roofs", which at least provide some compensation for the loss of wasteland habitat, and green walls, which can provide the vertical alternative to scrub habitat.

Licences for surveying protected species (also relevant for development licences)

| The animal listed are protected, to a varying extent, by the Wildlife and Countryside Act 1981 (as amended) and/or the Habitats Regulations 1994.

If, in the case of carrying out certain forms of surveys for these species, they are likely to require capturing in some way (for example a bottle trap for GCN), then a licence must be obtained from the appropriate SNCO before the survey takes place. References and appropriate experience are essential prerequisites for obtaining a licence.

The SNCOs aim to respond to a licence application within 15 days and, once issued, licences are valid for 12 months. | Species that are protected under Schedule 5 of the WCA and/or Wildlife Order (NI):
● otter * (1,2)
● natterjack toad* (1,2)
● great crested newt* (1,2)
● reptiles (*sand lizard and smooth snake) (1,2)
● bats* (1,2)
● dormice* (1,2)
● badgers (3)
● common newt (in NI only) (1)
● all nesting birds
● pine marten (1,2)
● red squirrel (1,2)
● water vole
● white-clawed crayfish
● protected species of invertebrates (large blue butterfly (1,2) – not NI)
● protected species of fish (*Atlantic sturgeon (1,2) – not NI).

(1) *Fully protected under UK law*
(2) *Protected under Habitats Regulations 1994 (and/or 1995 NI) and therefore a development licence may need to be obtained from Defra, SEERAD, the WA or EHS-NH (NI).*
(3) ***An SNCO development licence may be required for works affecting badgers.* |

UK LEGISLATION RELEVANT TO CONSTRUCTION AND WILDLIFE

The most important Acts and regulations are listed on the facing page. Further details of their provisions and of the other relevant legislation are set out in the Appendix (Legislation table).

The *Wildlife and Countryside Act 1981 (WCA)* is the principal piece of legislation protecting wildlife in Great Britain. It has undergone various revisions, including those made by the *Wildlife and Countryside (Amendment) Act 1985*, and the *Countryside and Rights of Way Act 2000*. Broadly, it seeks to protect individual species and habitats as Sites of Special Scientific Interest (SSSIs). All wild birds are given some protection during the breeding season, and other species are given different degrees of protection depending on their conservation status.

Don't be reckless

If you are planning works in an area that is suitable for birds protected under *Schedule 1* or animals protected under *Schedule 5* of the WCA 1981 *(as amended)* then *it is considered reasonable to expect that you should be aware of the risk of disturbing the species or destroying its breeding site.*

If you continue to carry out work without undertaking the necessary surveys or taking appropriate precautions then you are considered to be acting "recklessly" in contravention of the *WCA 1981* as amended by the *CRoW Act 2000*.

The *Conservation (Natural Habitats etc.) Regulations 1994* – also known as the "Habitats Regulations" – implement the *EU Habitats Directive* in Great Britain. The regulations require that sites of European Community importance are designated as Special Areas of Conservation (SACs). The regulations define "European nature conservation sites" as including, among others, SACs, and Special Protection Areas (SPAs), the latter being designated under the *Wild Birds Directive (1979)*. The *Habitats Directive* also lists a restricted number of animals and plants as European protected species.

The *Countryside and Rights of Way Act 2000* – the *CRoW Act 2000* applies only to England and Wales. It amends the WCA 1981 by, among other things, strengthening the protection given to SSSIs and other important wildlife sites, and placing a duty on government to take into account biodiversity action plans. The Act also makes it a criminal offence to *"recklessly disturb"* Schedule 1 nesting birds and certain species protected under Schedule 5 of the WCA. This has important implications for construction contractors. The *Nature Conservation (Scotland) Act 2004* makes similar amendments to the WCA 1981 for implementation in Scotland.

The *Protection of Badgers Act 1992* protects badgers and their setts. It extends to England, Scotland and Wales but not to Northern Ireland.

The *Town and Country Planning (Trees) Regulations 1999* (England and Wales only) includes provisions for protecting any tree, group of trees or woodland by allowing the local planning authority to place a Tree Preservation Order on them.

The *Hedgerow Regulations 1997* introduced arrangements for local planning authorities in England and Wales to protect important hedgerows in the countryside by controlling their removal through a system of notification. In some cases in now may be a criminal offence to remove a hedgerow without first notifying the local planning authority.

In **Northern Ireland** wildlife is principally protected by the *Wildlife (NI) Order 1985.* The *Environment (NI) Order 2003* provides protection for ASSIs (Areas of Special Scientific Interest – the Northern Ireland equivalent to SSSIs). Trees are protected under the *Planning (Tree Preservation Order) Regulations 1973* and the *Planning (Northern Ireland) Order 1991.*

WILDLIFE AND PLANNING POLICY

The planning system is also an important tool in wildlife conservation, and one that is particularly relevant to the construction industry. Local planning authorities are under various statutory obligations to take account of nature conservation when they determine planning applications.

Government at national and regional levels produce planning guidance and advice indicating how nature conservation issues should be addressed through the planning system. This guidance is in the form of:

- in England: planning policy guidance* (PPGs), mineral planning guidance* (MPGs) and regional planning guidance* (RPGs)

- in Scotland: national planning policy guidance* (NPPGs)

- in Wales: planning policy Wales (PPWs), planning advice notes (PANs) and technical advice notes (TANs)

- in Northern Ireland: planning policy statements (PPSs)

- and in circulars (issued by the Office of the Deputy Prime Minister in England, and by the Scottish Parliament and the National Assembly for Wales) and Government White Papers.

* Note that existing planning policy guidance is now being replaced by a new system of *planning policy statements*. Equally, mineral planning guidance will be replaced by *mineral planning statements* and regional planning guidance by *regional planning statements*.
In Scotland national planning policy guidance will be replaced by *Scottish planning policy* (SPP).

Many of these guidance notes refer to biodiversity and broader sustainability issues, and some deal with it specifically, for example **PPS 9 – Biodiversity and Geological Conservation.** In effect, these give guidance on the importance that government attaches to aspects of wildlife conservation and so assists local authorities to make decisions that may affect wildlife within their own areas.

At the local level, a development under the terms of the Planning Acts has to acquire planning permission from the local planning authority before it can proceed.

As a response to a planning application, the LPA may:

▨ refuse planning permission, in which case the developer can appeal

▨ grant planning permission without conditions (now very rare)

▨ grant planning permission but with conditions attached or with a negotiated agreement with the developer to ensure that certain obligations are met. (See box below).

Planning obligations or agreements (S.106 agreements in England and Wales, S.75 agreement in Scotland, Article 40 agreement in Northern Ireland) and conditions

Planning obligations or agreements can be made in England and Wales under the provisions of S.106 of The Town and Country Planning Act 1990, in Scotland under S.75 of The Town and Country Planning (Scotland) Act 1997 and in Northern Ireland under the Planning (NI) Order 1991. They are normally reached by agreement between the developer and the LPA, but in certain circumstances the LPA can impose obligations along with granting planning permission.	**Planning conditions** are similar to planning obligations, but should not be duplicated by them. They are normally used to avoid or mitigate for impacts on wildlife. The tests for planning conditions require that they are: ● necessary ● relevant to planning ● relevant to the development permitted ● enforceable ● precise ● reasonable in all other respects.
Obligations should: ● serve a planning purpose ● relate to the proposed development ● be related in scale and kind to the development proposed ● satisfy the test of reasonableness.	*(Circular 11/95, The Use of Conditions in Planning Permissions, DoE; Circular 1/97, Planning Obligations, DoE. Developing Naturally)*

BIODIVERSITY ACTION PLANS

Biodiversity Action Plans (BAPs) are another form of guidance that are increasing in importance. BAPs comprise species action plans (SAPs) and habitat action plans (HAPs) that state what is needed to conserve and enhance the status of certain wildlife species and habitats that are perceived to be under threat of long-term damage, decline or loss.

Planning permission achieved – what next?

> If your site already has planning permission, ensure that you are aware of any planning conditions or legal agreements that may have been made.
>
> Ecological conditions may refer to carrying out site surveys, to fencing off sensitive areas of the site before work begins or to seasonal constraints on work. Very often they include measures to mitigate for any loss or damage to wildlife and habitats.
>
> Check with the local planning authority to see if BAP habitats and species are included within any planning policies.

BAPs have begun to appear at a variety of different levels, ie national BAPs, county BAPs, London borough BAPs and district council BAPs. Important governmental organisations have also produced their own BAPs, for example the Highways Agency. Further information on biodiversity action plans can be found at www.ukbap.org.uk

The targets set in a local BAP often refer to habitats or species that may not be thought of as rare or threatened at the national or local level, and may not be protected in any way. In developing a site you may not be affecting any land designated or supporting protected species, but it may comprise habitats or support species for which there is a local action plan (HAP or SAP).

BAPs – what you should do

> It is important that any impacts on BAP habitats or species are kept to a minimum, as is similarly advocated for designated habitats or protected species. In terms of any enhancement or habitat creation, assisting a BAP in meeting its target will be seen as the right way to proceed and can result in the development being more favourably received.
>
> The construction industry can contribute to HAPs and SAPs irrespective of what they are doing in relation to a particular development. Companies are now investing money into specific plans for a species or a habitat that they have adopted as their own. This not only helps wildlife, but it is also good public relations, and an excellent point of interest for employees.

Survey and assessment – what should you do?

Key actions for the five main players usually involved in construction projects are set out below. Actions highlighted in red are of particular importance.

Client	Planners	Designers	Contractors
• Carry out early scoping studies, ecological data collection and research and environmental assessment to assist your site selection process. • Avoid, wherever possible, proposing development that will impact on designated sites and other ecologically sensitive areas. • Include a commitment to wildlife conservation in your environmental policy statement, cover it in your environmental management system and ensure you deliver it. • Consider sponsorship of biodiversity action plan species or habitats. • Ensure, through contractual arrangements, that your designer and contractor are required to take full account of your environmental policy and requirements, and of site ecology in their work. • Consider appointing an ecologist to act as a client representative through the construction phase.	• Ensure that ecological issues are given due consideration in the plans for any development. • Allow sufficient time for any necessary ecological surveys to be carried out. Ensure that they are carried out at the appropriate time of year, and that they are sufficiently detailed to characterise the ecology of the site and to predict impacts and opportunities accurately. If you work for a local authority: • ensure that your local plan contains clear and achievable policies to protect and enhance wildlife within the local plan area (refer to the relevant planning guidance) • where relevant, impose planning conditions and obligations to safeguard ecological interests and to ensure adequate mitigation, compensation or enhancement for any impacts of the development • utilise ecological expertise to help determine planning applications and impose planning conditions. • Promote any opportunities to contribute towards local biodiversity action plan targets.	• Note the results of any ecological assessment that may be available and its recommendations to "avoid – mitigate – compensate – enhance" • Where possible, design the project to avoid or minimise adverse impacts on local ecology and maximise enhancements. • Consider integrating ecological features, for example climbing plants, bird nestboxes, and bat boxes, within any buildings or structures. • Ensure that landscape design reflects local ecology and uses locally sourced plants wherever possible. • Use the "design strategy for incorporating nature conservation into development" that is to be found in *Developing Naturally* (Oxford 2000).	• Ensure that you know, and understand, the ecological constraints and opportunities that a project offers at the earliest possible opportunity (preferably before you submit your tender!) and that appropriate measures are incorporated into method statements. • When appointed, consider whether a pre-construction ecological survey may be necessary, for example, for protected species or for invasive plants such as Japanese knotweed. • If the project has ecologically sensitive habitats or species, protect these with fencing and signage, and consider appointing an ecologist to carry out an Ecological Watching Brief or Ecological Clerk of Works role during construction. **Specialist sub-contractors** (for example earthworks contractors) • Ensure that the principal contractor (or your client if different) provides you with any ecological information on the site. Understand the constraints and opportunities that this information may impose on your work.

USE THIS SITE GUIDE TO INFORM YOUR STAFF

The consequences of getting it wrong

Role	What if?	Result	What should happen?
Clients (including housebuilders and developers)	• Important site for wildlife? • Client's team have no understanding or commitment to wildlife issues?	• No planning permission • Planning permission delayed • Bad publicity	• Avoid sites designated as being important for wildlife wherever possible • Select a team with understanding and commitment to wildlife conservation. • Instruct your team to ensure that wildlife is taken into account in the design, implementation and subsequent operation of any construction projects. • At a minimum, ensure that they are instructed to comply fully with all wildlife legislation. • Make staff aware by using this guide
Planners/ designers	• Commission wrong surveys at wrong time of year? • Don't leave enough time for surveys or for acquiring licences? • Ignore wildlife issues?	• No useful information collected. Surveys have to be repeated • Planning permission refused or delayed because of inadequate information • Opportunities for mitigating impacts and wildlife enhancement overlooked	• Ensure that all relevant surveys and assessment of the wildlife interest of a site are given ample time to be undertaken at the right time of year and that the results are incorporated within any mitigation compensation or enhancement schemes. • Where possible avoid important wildlife areas within or adjoining a site. • Ensure that mitigation, compensation or enhancement schemes are incorporated within the final scheme design. • Make staff aware by using this guide
Contractors	• Not aware of wildlife issues on site? • Wildlife issues not taken into account by construction programme? • Indirect impacts of construction not taken into account?	• Delays and associated costs, potential fines or imprisonment, especially if protected species are affected • Delays to programme and associated costs • Unwittingly harm wildlife and suffer the consequential delays, fines, bad press etc	• Be aware of any undertakings made by the client, planner or designer in respect of wildlife. • Ensure that you understand the wildlife opportunities and constraints that the construction site brings, and that your construction programme takes them fully into account. • If necessary utilise ecologists to carry out a Watching Brief. • Make staff aware by using this guide
THE SOLUTION: KNOW YOUR SITE AND YOUR WILDLIFE!			

Case study

Although an old badger sett had been cordoned off with chestnut paling fence on this construction project, the driver of a tracked excavator, visible in the distance, crashed through the fence – narrowly missing the set, and potential prosecution.

This shows very dramatically how important it is that all site staff are informed about sensitive wildlife and wildlife habitats on site.

Lessons that can be learned from incidents like this are:

- fencing off on its own may not be enough

- areas to be left alone must be well signposted

- all staff and sub-contractors should be briefed

- it takes only a few moments for heavy construction plant to do severe damage that cannot be undone.

Licensing

LICENSING AND PROTECTED SPECIES

There are principally three types of activity for which a licence may be necessary when dealing with protected species :

1   Surveys (See box p22).

2   Development.

3   Conservation and other issues.

For detailed guidance on specific species see species briefings (pages 42–157).

Where applicable these licences are issued by Defra, WA, SEERAD or the EHS-NH (NI), or where relevant by the SNCO.

DEVELOPMENT LICENCE

If, as part of an approved development project, it is planned to capture, disturb, uproot and/or relocate or damage the habitat of a species protected under the *Habitats Regulations 1994 or 1995 (NI)* (European Protected Species such as bats, great crested newts, otters etc), a "development licence" must be obtained. Before applying for a licence, appropriate surveys must have been carried out to ensure that the proposed work is based on accurate information. Licence applications should be made to Defra, WA, SEERAD or EHS-NH(NI).

Applications must satisfy the following three tests:

1   The development is for the purpose of *"preserving public health or public safety or other imperative reasons of overriding public interest including those of a social or economic nature and beneficial consequences of primary importance for the environment"*.

2   The licence granting authority is satisfied *"that there is no satisfactory alternative"*.

3   The development will not be *"detrimental to the maintenance of the population of the species at a favourable conservation status in their natural range"*.

To meet these tests the authority will require the planning position of a development to be fully resolved!

In considering the third test, the authority will take advice from the relevant SNCO who will use the method statement to inform their decision.

The SNCO and the LPA are given 20 working days to fulfil requests for information and the licensing authority aims to issue decisions within 10 working days of receipt of all necessary information.

The whole process should be complete within 30 working days, but delays can occur. Licenses should be obtained well in advance since related mitigation works are likely to be needed before construction starts.

In **Northern Ireland** all development applications go through the Department of Environment and get passed on automatically from the planning department to EHS-NH who then assess the application from an environmental perspective and are responsible for the granting of all licences in relation to wild animals.

DEVELOPMENT WORKS AFFECTING BADGERS

Where development will *"interfere"* with a badger sett a licence has to be obtained from the SNCO. The term "interference" includes damaging or destroying a badger sett, obstructing any entrance to a sett or disturbing a badger when it is occupying a sett.

The SNCO to which you apply will require:

- a method statement which clearly describes how the proposed development work will interfere with the badger setts and also demonstrates how any mitigation work will be carried out where applicable

- written authority from the owner to permit entry to representatives of the SNCO for monitoring/inspecting work

- written authority from the owner that the applicant is acting on their behalf

- copy of the planning permission

- references from two people who can vouch for the suitability of the applicant (unless a similar licence has been held in the last three years).

The SNCOs aim to respond to license applications within 15 days.

CONSERVATION LICENCE

A further form of licence is a "conservation licence". Conservation licences are generally issued by EN, SNH, CCW or EHS-NH(NI) to protect a population that is under threat because of natural degradation of its habitat rather than cases where development will result in loss of animals and/or habitats. Licences are considered for the sole purpose of improving the habitat or conservation status of the species for which the licence is being sought.

Exceptions may occur where development works will impact on white-clawed (Atlantic stream) crayfish throughout the UK, and possibly for other non-European protected species in Northern Ireland (eg common newt, common lizard). In these cases, SNCOs may consider it appropriate to grant a conservation licence for a development "where doing so will be of a conservation advantage".

The SNCO issuing the licence will require the same information as is needed for a survey licence application.

Guidance on the optimal timing for carrying out specialist ecological surveys and mitigation

The charts that follow are not definitive and are intended to provide an indication only. The timing of surveys and animal activity will be dependent on factors such as weather conditions. Please consult the species briefing section (pages 42–157) of this guide for more detailed information, including species distribution.

* Where survey techniques involve the capture, handling or disturbance of certain protected species then only licensed persons can undertake surveys; personal survey and monitoring licences are obtained from English Nature, Countryside Council for Wales, Environment and Heritage Service (NI) or Scottish Natural Heritage.

** Where mitigation involves the killing, capture, injury and/or disturbance of European Protected Species and/or the damage, destruction or obstruction of their habitats, a development licence must be obtained from the Department for Food and Rural Affairs (England), Scottish Executive's Environment and Rural Affairs Department, Welsh Assembly (Countryside Division) or the Environment and Heritage Service Northern Ireland. Licences will be granted only to persons who have proven competence in dealing with the species concerned. Development licence applications take approximately 30 days to be processed by government departments. Where mitigation works need to be conducted under licence before works begin, licence applications will need to be submitted considerably earlier.

Key

	Recommended survey time
	No surveys
	Mitigation conducted at these times
	Mitigations works restricted

Group		License required?	J	F	M	A	M	J	J	A	S	O	N	D
Habitats/ vegetation	Surveys	N	Mosses & lichens. No other detailed plant surveys – Phase 1 surveys only (least suitable time)		Detailed habitat assessment surveys. Surveys for higher plants and ferns							Mosses & lichens. No other detailed plant surveys – Phase 1 surveys only (least suitable time)		
	Mitigation	N	Planting and translocation									Planting and translocation		
Birds	Surveys	N	Winter birds		Breeding birds/migrant species		Breeding birds			Breeding birds/migrant species		Winter birds		
	Mitigation	N	Clearance works may be conducted at this time but must stop immediately if any nesting birds are found		No mitigation for majority of species							Clearance works may be conducted at this time but must stop immediately if any nesting birds are found		
					No clearance or construction works that may affect nesting birds									
Badgers	Surveys	*	All survey methods – best time in early autumn/winter											
	Mitigation	**	Building of artificial setts. No disturbance of existing setts				Stopping up or destruction of existing setts							See Jan to June
Bats	Surveys	*	Inspection of hibernation, tree and building roosts		Roost inspections. Emergence and Activity surveys								Inspection of hibernation roosts	
	Mitigation	**	Works on maternity roosts	Works on maternity roosts until mid-May, Works on hibernation roosts from mid-March			Works on hibernation roosts only				Hibernation roosts until November. Maternity roosts from mid-September		Works on maternity roosts	

		License required?	J	F	M	A	M	J	J	A	S	O	N	D
Dormice	Surveys	*	Nut searches (sub-optimum time)				Cage traps, hair tube and nest box surveys to mid-October. Nut searches from September (optimum time from Sept-Dec). Nest searches (optimum time Sept-March)						Nut searches and nest searches (optimum time)	
	Mitigation	**	No clearance works				Clearance works (sub-optimum time)	No clearance works			Clearance works to early Oct (optimum time)		No clearance works	
Otters	Surveys	*	Surveys for otters can potentially be conducted all year round, though vegetation cover and weather conditions may limit the times at which surveys can be carried out											
	Mitigation	**	Mitigation can potentially be conducted in any month, but is likely to be restricted where otters are found to be breeding											
Pine martens	Surveys	*	Surveys may be conducted all year round, weather permitting. Optimum time is spring and summer. Surveys for breeding dens from March to May											
	Mitigation	**	Works in areas of pine marten habitats and dens	Avoid all works in pine marten habitats									Works in areas of pine marten habitats and dens	
Red squirrels	Surveys	*	Surveys may be conducted all year round, weather permitting. Surveys for breeding females from December to September. Optimum time is spring and summer.											
	Mitigation	**	Reduced activity	Initial surveys possible	Avoid all works in red squirrel habitat							Works should preferably be conducted at this time	Initial surveys possible	Reduced activity / Avoid all works in red squirrel habitat
Water voles (n/a in NI)	Surveys	N[2]	All survey methods can be used in this period, though vegetation cover and weather conditions may limit times at which survey can be carried out. (Optimum time Mar-Jun)											
	Mitigation	*		Avoid all works in water vole habitat				Avoid all works in water vole habitat			Avoid all works in water vole habitat			
Sand lizards, smooth snakes (n/a in NI)[1] and common lizards	Surveys	*		No surveys – reptiles in hibernation	Active surveys from March to June and in September/October. Surveys are limited by high temperatures during July/August. Peak survey months are April, May and September								No surveys – reptiles in hibernation	
	Mitigation	**	Scrub clearance	Capture and translocation programmes can be conducted only while reptiles are active (March to June and September/October). Trapping is limited by high temperatures during July/August. Scrub clearance									Scrub clearance	

2 The extent of legal protection of the water vole is currently under review. It has been proposed to fully protect water voles as well as their habitats

		Licence required?	J	F	M	A	M	J	J	A	S	O	N	D
Other reptiles	**Surveys**	N	No surveys – reptiles in hibernation	Activity surveys from March to June and in September/October. Surveys are limited by high temperatures in July/August. Peak survey months are April, May and September									No surveys – reptiles in hibernation
	Mitigation	N	Scrub clearance	Capture and translocation programmes can be conducted only while reptiles are active (March to June and September/October). Trapping is limited by high temperatures during July/August. Scrub clearance								Scrub clearance	
Great crested newts (n/a in NI)	**Surveys**	*	No surveys – newts in hibernation	No surveys – newts in hibernation	Pond surveys for adults: mid-March to mid-June. Surveys must include visits undertaken between mid-April and mid-May. Egg surveys April to mid-June. Larvae surveys from mid-May. Terrestrial habitat surveys.				Larvae surveys to mid-August Terrestrial habitat surveys		Terrestrial habitat surveys		No surveys – newts in hibernation	No surveys – newts in hibernation
	Mitigation	**	No trapping of newts Pond management only	No trapping of newts Pond management only	Newt trapping programmes in ponds and on land						Newt trapping on land only		No trapping of newts Pond management only	No trapping of newts Pond management only
Natterjack toads	**Surveys**	*	No surveys – toads in hibernation	No surveys – toads in hibernation	Surveys of breeding ponds for adults				Surveys for adults on land			No surveys – toads in hibernation	No surveys – toads in hibernation
	Mitigation	**	Pond management works	Pond management works	Trapping of adults in ponds from April to July. Trapping of adults on land. Trapping of tadpoles from May to early September							Pond management works	Pond management works
White-clawed crayfish	**Surveys**	*	Reduced activity	Reduced activity	Surveys can be undertaken	Avoid surveys (females are releasing young)		Optimum time for surveys				Reduced activity	Reduced activity
	Mitigation	***	Avoid capture programmes (low activity levels may lead to animals being easily missed)	Avoid capture programmes (low activity levels may lead to animals being easily missed)	Exclusion of crayfish from construction areas	Avoid capture programmes	Exclusion of crayfish from construction areas					Avoid capture programmes (low activity levels may lead to animals being easily missed)	Avoid capture programmes (low activity levels may lead to animals being easily missed)
Fish	**Surveys**	*	For coastal, river and stream-dwelling species, the time of surveys will depend on the migration pattern of the species concerned. Where surveys require information on breeding, the timing of surveys will need to coincide with the breeding period, which may be summer or winter months, depending on the species.											
	Mitigation	**	Mitigation for the protection of watercourses is required at all times of the year. Mitigation for particular fish species will need to be timed to avoid the breeding season. This varies from species to species.											

*** Where mitigation involves the capture of white-clawed crayfish, a conservation licence must be obtained from English Nature, Countryside Council for Wales, Environment and Heritage Service (NI) or Scottish Natural Heritage. Licences will be granted only to persons who have proven competence in dealing with the species concerned.

Roles of the contractor and ecologist

Well, you now have a good feel for what the issues are all about, but there still seems an awful lot to know and do. So, what should happen when you have a site and it has some wildlife importance?

First of all, don't panic! There is a way forward. Second, don't forget, it is not the purpose of this document to turn construction professionals into ecologists, so consider engaging one – see below.

Site ecologist with a newly constructed bat chamber

Third, if you are a client or designer, review the previous chapter specifically in relation to your project, commission appropriate surveys and build the results into your design.

If you are at construction stage, and are concerned about wildlife issues on your site, do not hesitate to commission a pre-construction ecological survey and assessment. This ensures that you are fully aware of all the issues and it will almost certainly reduce any difficulties you may encounter later on.

ECOLOGY AND SITE ENVIRONMENTAL MANAGEMENT

Environmental management systems, such as those in line with the requirements of ISO 14001, are now very much a part of the day-to-day workings of major construction industry companies. Contractors in particular are employing the principles of EMS at the site level to generate what are often called site environmental management plans (or something similar) to help them, among other things, to manage and reduce the adverse environmental impacts of their work as well as to maximise the opportunities for improvements.

To comply with EMS requirements, environmental work procedures will have to be prepared and these may well include **ecological procedures**. These generally consider the following points:

- legislative, contractual and third party requirements, including licences or consents

- ecological aspects of the site

- what needs to be checked or done, for example, to or for species or habitats, including invasive plants

- when the actions are needed – time of year, frequency of visits

- any company certification procedures

- by whom the work is to be done and who will be responsible if the ecologist is not on site – for example an environmental technician, general foreman or someone else

- defined responsibilities

- reporting requirements

- contact details for important personnel and organisations, including relevant third parties.

Included within the reporting system may be company **ecological permits** or **certificates** (in addition to legally necessary licences). These are forms for recording the measures undertaken at a specific location or against a specific works operation that has ecological implications. In certain cases, works may not be able to proceed until an ecologist has signed off the permit or certificate, recording his or her satisfaction with the ecological safeguards put in place.

WHAT IS THE ROLE OF THE CONTRACTOR'S ECOLOGIST?

Construction – if undertaken badly – can have a devastating effect on ecology, and in a frighteningly short space of time. The machines used in construction today are very powerful and are able to shift tonnes of material in minutes. However, they can also be put to good effect in enhancing and creating habitats where necessary.

Many of the issues that determine the extent of these impacts will have been settled at the planning and design stages. The role of the contractor's ecologist, therefore, is to focus on those practical elements of construction that are related to wildlife and ecology (See table p15), and in particular to:

- ensure that all the ecological aspects of the site are known and understood

- ensure that legal duties, planning requirements and contract conditions are adhered to

- if appropriate, ensure that ecological procedures following best practice guidelines are drawn up and monitored

- provide ecological guidance – or ensure that it is on hand – to assist construction workers

- advise the contractor when specialists are needed, for example a badger specialist

- undertake training.

Often, the role of the contractor's ecologist is defined as an **ecological clerk of works, environmental supervisor** or as carrying out an **ecological watching brief**. Broadly these terms mean the ecologist is there to safeguard the contractor's position in terms of dealing with ecological aspects of the work.

Actual work on site for the ecologist will require working closely with various members of staff both in offices and out on site, including in close proximity with heavy pieces of machinery and all the health and safety implications that that infers. It may mean undertaking physical work or at least organising it or directing it where circumstances necessitate.

When using ecologists, make sure they are involved with and apprised of all aspects of the development project. They cannot do their job properly if they do not know what is being proposed or have not seen the plans.

You are about to start construction – what should you do next?
(After Oxford 2000)

Information provision

- obtain existing information on the site and its wildlife interest from the client, the designer, the local planning authority or third parties

- consider carrying out a pre-construction ecological survey.

Timing of works

- Provide a timetable to show:
  - when specific measures will be implemented (such as fencing, training etc)
  - phasing of construction activities to avoid critical periods (including legal constraints, eg nesting season).

Avoiding impacts during construction

- review planning consents and contract documentation for any ecological constraints, conditions and obligations and ensure that these are adequately addressed in tender documents, method statements etc

- obtain and comply with any necessary licences for dealing with or working near protected species. Obtaining licences in some cases may take months and, in extreme cases, may be refused.

- ensure that you have programmed in sufficient time to deal with protected species. Certain animals cannot be disturbed once they are breeding or cannot be removed from a site if it happens to be the wrong time of year

- review the location and timing of all construction activities to avoid harm to important wildlife features

- training and awareness: provide information to all site staff explaining the importance of sensitive features, including the use of this guide. Make sure they are aware of the roles and responsibilities of key personnel, such as the project ecologist

- erect information or warning signs for site personnel and include details of who should be contacted for further information

- erect fences to protect sensitive nature conservation areas and other features, including areas contaminated by invasive plants such as Japanese knotweed, areas with nesting birds, protected trees etc

- define roles and responsibilities for carrying out a watching brief over wildlife aspects on site (may include appointment of an ecological clerk of works)

- consider temporary management of existing wildlife features during construction (eg hay cuts)

- regularly review mitigation measures throughout the construction period and monitor their effectiveness. Measures may need repeating or modifying (for example regular grass cutting to exclude reptiles from construction areas)

- guard against vandalism (eg security fencing around equipment and/or materials that could cause pollution)

- draw up procedures to avoid pollution incidents, for example from fuel spillages or site run-off.

You are about to start construction (Cont.)

- be sure to have contingency measures in place for unexpected incidents (eg discovery of protected species during construction)
- have emergency measures in place for accidents (such as pollution incidents) and other measures (eg for repair of damaged features).

Responsible persons & lines of communication

Provide details of personnel and lines of communication necessary to implement the construction mitigation measures, including:

- compliance with
  - regulations and legal consents
  - planning conditions,
  - contractual arrangements relating to nature conservation
- installation of physical protection measures
- provision of training and information for staff about the importance of nature conservation features on site (use this guide!)

- regular monitoring of environmental procedures, and inspection and maintenance of physical measures
- on-going monitoring and implementation of contingency measures in the event of an accident or occurrence of other potentially damaging incidents.

Documentation

- ensure that the points mentioned above are covered by ecological procedures or a site environmental management plan
- complete weekly or monthly reports stating issues examined and actions required
- maintain records and periodically review operations to identify problems and to take remedial action
- audit plans, reports and records to ensure conformance with established procedures, legislation and good practice.

Species briefing – introduction

This section summarises some issues that are common to all species. This information should be read in conjunction with the following species briefings.

These briefings cover the majority of commonly found species that are protected by the law. The latter six – feral pigeon, foxes, grey squirrel, invasive plants, mink and rats – are differentiated by titles in red (as opposed to green for the protected species). These are species that are often considered as potential pests on construction sites and which, generally, have a very different legal position from the protected species.

Construction professionals may be asking themselves "Is there anything that we can do on site at any time of year?" However, it should be remembered that many of the following briefings deal with animals that are protected precisely because they are rare and their distribution in the UK is limited, and they are unlikely to be found on every piece of developable land. Where protected species are present on a site there are, in most circumstances, actions that can be taken to avoid, mitigate or compensate for any impacts.

The key factor is to allow sufficient time in the programme for carrying out the necessary surveys and other associated work. If that is done, then any protected species issues can be dealt with comfortably within the project time frame, and a successful outcome for wildlife and construction achieved.

CONSTRUCTION AND WILDLIFE – THE NEED TO PLAN AHEAD

Planning guidance across the UK makes it clear that nature conservation is a material consideration in determining a planning application.

SNCOs advise that surveys should be undertaken *before seeking planning permission*, so that development is designed to avoid any impacts on protected species.

Leaving surveys until a later stage increases the risk that plans for the development will have to be redesigned or halted (temporarily or permanently) if protected species are found.

In such cases, works would have to wait until surveys and any mitigation have been completed. This process can be very complex, time-consuming and can usually be conducted only at specific times of year – *in most cases delays will last several weeks or months*.

To avoid extensive delays, surveys should be conducted as early as possible in the planning process as, if protected species are found:

● alternative sites or changes to the development footprint may need to be considered

● mitigation may need to be designed and planned (where impacts are unavoidable)

● a development licence, a conservation licence, and/or consents from the EA etc, may need to be obtained (where required)

● mitigation may need to be set in place.

The above points will need to be completed before the start of any works that will impact on protected species.

It is not of benefit to either species conservation or the construction industry to rely on last minute mitigation.

Translocation

Moving protected species "out of the way" is by no means the easy option. On the contrary, it can be extremely expensive and time-consuming to achieve and can often result in works being delayed by a year or more. Delays are lengthened because capture programmes are often seasonally restricted and trapping may be required for more than one activity season.

Time and money will also need to be invested in locating receptor sites and/or habitat creation, and post-translocation monitoring.

For many species it remains arguable whether or not translocation can be used successfully as part of mitigation for development. SNCOs are likely to accept translocation as a mitigation measure only when every alternative option has been explored.

Post development monitoring

Mitigation agreements will need to include a monitoring plan so that the success (or otherwise) of mitigation measures can be assessed. The duration of monitoring may last from a few weeks or months to a number of years. Generally the more significant the impact (and consequently the level of mitigation), the longer the period of monitoring.

Disclaimer – species briefing

The following species briefings are by no means the complete or final word and should be used only as a general guide. If any of the species described is present on a site with which you are involved, then seek further information by utilising the references quoted in the main section, by consulting the SNCOs or by utilising the skills of a qualified and suitably experienced ecologist. Note that planning policies, guidance notes and biodiversity action plans may influence your approach to various wildlife species.

The legal guidance given on each species is only a general guide to the provisions of the law. Furthermore, wildlife legislation is continually reviewed and updated. Please consult the relevant legislation for the complete wording and to ensure the latest information is taken into account.

Common amphibians

Great crested newts (*Triturus cristatus*) and natterjack toads (*Bufo calamita*) are both fully protected amphibian species and are dealt with separately. The advice provided within this section refers to cases where surveys have shown that great crested newts and natterjack are not present.

IDENTIFYING COMMON AMPHIBIANS

Four of the most widespread amphibian species native to the UK are the common frog (*Rana temporaria*), common toad (*Bufo bufo*), common (or smooth) newt (*Triturus vulgaris*) and palmate newt (*Triturus helveticus*). Common toad and palmate newt do not occur in Northern Ireland.

Common toad

Legal protection

In England, Scotland and Wales the common frog, common toad, smooth newt and palmate newt are all protected against sale, trade etc under the **Wildlife and Countryside Act 1981.**

Palmate newt

In Northern Ireland the common frog receives similar protection as in the rest of the UK, while the common newt is *fully protected* under the **Wildlife (NI) Order 1985**, making it illegal to:

Common frog

- ▨ intentionally kill, injure or capture common newts

- ▨ intentionally disturb common newts when in a place of shelter or protection

- ▨ intentionally damage, destroy or obstruct access to any places used for shelter or protection (whether occupied or not)

Common newt

- ▨ sell, barter, exchange, transport or offer for sale common newts (or any part thereof) unless under licence.

The legislation covers all life stages, ie eggs, larvae, juveniles and adults.

Other legislation and nature conservation guidance

These species are also protected from cruelty by the **Protection of Animals Act 1911** and the **Welfare of Animals Act (NI) 1972**.

All four species are of conservation concern, primarily due to habitat loss, and are often are included within local biodiversity action plans.

Licensing for development

In England, Scotland and Wales development works affecting these species do not require a licence.

In Northern Ireland, there is no provision for licensing of works that will affect **common newts**. Evidence will be required that all reasonable effort was made to avoid breaking the law. This includes proof of adequate surveys and mitigation measures.

EA, SEPA or EHS-EP(NI) must be consulted wherever development works will affect watercourses or wetlands.

Practical measures for dealing with these species on site

Before conducting any works on any waterbodies, surveys of ponds and adjacent habitat must be conducted to assess whether any protected amphibian species are present.

In Northern Ireland, where survey methods involve capture or disturbance of **common newts,** a *survey licence* must be obtained from EHS-NH(NI).

Even if no protected species is present, destruction of waterbodies should be avoided wherever possible. If destruction proves necessary, it should be conducted over the winter months (November to January), to minimise the impact on amphibian populations.

Pond drainage should be conducted using methods that minimise the risk of injury to animals that are overwintering in the pond.

AMPHIBIANS – NATURAL HISTORY

Although they use ponds to breed, all species of British amphibian spend a large proportion of their time on land, where they can be found at any time of year.

The eggs of amphibians are laid in water and hatch into tadpoles or larvae. After several weeks or months they change (or metamorphose) into juveniles, which have a similar body shape to adults, only much smaller. From juvenile stage onwards amphibians can live both on land and in water.

In general, amphibians use ponds between February and August. Most leave the water in late spring/early summer, but some may remain in water during the winter.

Palmate and common newts

Both newt species show similar behaviour:

- they overwinter on land, during which time they are relatively inactive but some individuals may remain in ponds

- in early spring most adults migrate to breeding ponds. Some, individuals ready to reproduce for the first time in the following spring, may migrate to breeding ponds in autumn

- metamorphosis of larvae takes place from July to September, and most of the juvenile newts then remain on land until they are ready to breed 2–3 years later

- larvae from eggs laid late in the season may overwinter in the pond and emerge the next spring.

	Key
	Peak numbers
	Moderate numbers
	Few individuals

Common and palmate newt	J	F	M	A	M	J	J	A	S	O	N	D
Adults active												
Mating and breeding												
Larvae in pond												
Metamorphosis												

Common frog

The common frog is active throughout more months of the year than any other British amphibian.

- it hibernates in mud at the bottom of ponds or uses terrestrial refugia such as compost heaps and in mild winters it often does not fully hibernate

- frog populations assemble at ponds for spawning in early spring, but in the south-west this occurs earlier than in the north-east and upland regions, where spawning can start as late as April. In Cornwall, on the other hand, it can take place as early as November

- after spawning, the frogs disperse from the spawning area but may stay in and around the pond for the rest of the year

- following metamorphosis of tadpoles, juveniles disperse from the breeding pond and feed on land until they reach maturity.

Key	
■ (dark)	Peak numbers
▨ (medium)	Moderate numbers
□ (light)	Few individuals

Common frog	J	F	M	A	M	J	J	A	S	O	N	D
Adults active	Few	Few	Peak	Peak	Peak	Peak	Peak	Peak	Peak	Moderate		Few
Mating and breeding			Moderate	Peak	Moderate							
Tadpoles in pond				Moderate	Peak	Peak	Peak	Moderate	Few			
Metamorphosis						Moderate	Peak	Moderate				

Common toad

Common toads enter the water for a short period only in spring. Breeding times vary from year to year, depending on weather conditions.

- migration to breeding ponds starts in autumn, is then interrupted by the hibernation period, and is completed in spring.

Common toad	J	F	M	A	M	J	J	A	S	O	N	D
Adults active		Few	Moderate	Peak	Peak	Peak	Peak	Peak	Peak	Moderate		
Mating and breeding			Moderate	Peak	Few							
Tadpoles in pond				Few	Peak	Peak	Moderate					
Metamorphosis						Few	Peak	Moderate				

If fully protected amphibian species (eg great crested newt) are found on site after works have started, *works in the area must stop immediately*. Works may need to be delayed until mitigation can be conducted at the appropriate time of year.

Vegetation clearance where protected species are known to be absent

Amphibians, particularly when very young or hibernating, are very likely to be injured during vegetation clearance using strimmers etc. Wherever possible this should be undertaken during the autumn, when animals are active but not breeding.

If possible, works should be avoided during the migration periods in February/March, and in late summer when young are leaving the water.

Grass height should be left at a minimum of 10 cm wherever possible.

When clearing sites, dismantle all sheltering places, such as rock piles and logs etc, by hand and place any animals in a cool, damp, sheltered place away from danger. Take particular care in winter – animals may be hibernating within rock-piles and vegetation, and are highly vulnerable to killing and injury.

Positive impacts through development

Opportunities to improve habitat for amphibians as part of landscaping and overall scheme design include:

- creation of ponds

- planting of wildlife corridors to create links to other areas of habitat

- provision of tunnels under roads, in conjuction with fences to funnel amphibians towards the tunnels.

Keeping within the law: common newts in NI

In Northern Ireland, to enable appropriate time-tabling of development works on sites where common newts are present, the following three points should be considered:

1 Pond surveys can be conducted only in spring and early summer. Surveys on land should be undertaken between late February and early October, though not during hot and dry periods.

2 Where common newts are shown to be present, EHS-NH(NI) require that impacts are avoided where possible, either through the use of alternative sites or re-design of the works. Where impacts are completely unavoidable, mitigation measures will need to be agreed and set in place before works go ahead. The timing of mitigation works may be restricted, for instance capture programmes in ponds will be restricted to spring and early summer, and capture programmes on land can be carried out only between February and early October.

3 To avoid prosecution under the Wildlife (NI) Order 1985, wherever works will impact on common newts there must be evidence that every reasonable effort was made to avoid breaking the law – including proof of adequate surveys and mitigation plans. Mitigation measures should be agreed with EHS-NH(NI).

Where to go for further help and guidance

Organisations that can be contacted for expert advice on amphibians:

- SNCOs
- Herpetological Conservation Trust
- Froglife
- wildlife trusts.

Fully protected species

Any of the above amphibian species may be found living side-by-side with the great crested newt (GCN) or, on rarer occasions, the natterjack toad. These species receive full protection under the *Wildlife and Countryside Act 1981* and the *Habitats Regulations 1994*. It is illegal to kill, injure, capture or disturb natterjack toads or GCN or the places they use for shelter and protection (for more information on these species see other briefings in this section).

GCN are almost twice the size of the other newt species, reaching a length of up to 19 cm, though

The great crested newt is fully protected

juvenile GCN may be mistaken for one of the smaller newt species.

If in any doubt about the identification of the species you have found, do not capture or disturb it, as this may be against the law. Consult an expert.

Badgers

IDENTIFYING BADGERS

What do they look like?

Adult badgers (*Meles meles*) grow up to a metre long. They have a stout body with grey fur, short black legs and a short white tail. The face is white with broad black stripes.

Habitat requirements

Badgers are found in towns and in the countryside in England, Wales, Northern Ireland and Scotland. In England they are most common in the south-west, but rare in East Anglia.

Ideal badger territory includes a combination of deciduous woodland and pasture.

Badgers live in underground tunnels and chambers known as a "sett". To dig their setts badgers need light, well-drained soils, often on sloping ground and usually with some degree of scrub and tree cover. A sett may consist of 1–12 holes or more. All setts are legally protected irrespective of the number of holes.

Badger setts are found in rural and suburban areas with possible locations including road embankments, caves, mines, refuse tips, gardens and under buildings.

What do we need to know about badgers?

Legal protection

Under the *Protection of Badgers Act 1992 and the Wildlife Order (NI) 1985*, it is illegal to:

- wilfully kill, injure, take, possess or cruelly treat a badger – or attempt to do so

- intentionally or recklessly damage, destroy or obstruct access to a badger sett (whether or not there is a badger in it at the time)

- disturb a badger while it is occupying a sett

- sell, keep or mark a healthy badger or possess any dead badger or part thereof.

Under the legislation not only setts are protected, but *"any structure or place which displays signs indicating current use by a badger"*. In addition to a more "traditional" sett, this can include parts of buildings, outbuildings, sheds, culverts, hollow trees etc.

Other legislation and nature conservation guidance

Badgers are also protected under the *Wild Mammals (Protection) Act 1996* and the *Welfare of Animals Act (NI) 1972*, which protect animals against cruelty. The badger and many of its feeding habitats are frequently included within local biodiversity action plans.

Licensing for development

Where development will interfere with a sett, an *SNCO badger licence* must be obtained from EN, CCW, EHS-NH(NI) or SNH. This will be granted only to a suitably-qualified ecologist and will depend on evidence of adequate surveys and mitigation plans. Interfering with a badger sett includes damaging or destroying a sett, obstructing any entrance to a sett and disturbing a badger when it is occupying a sett. Licences can take up to 15 days or more to be granted by SNCOs.

Badger signs

- Badger tunnels are at least 25 cm wide, broader than they are high, with a rounded or flattened oval shape. They often have large spoil heaps immediately outside.

- At tunnel entrances look for badger hairs (coarse hairs, white at the ends and black in the middle), traces of food (eg corn husks) or bedding (grass etc), and badger footprints.

- Also look for well-worn paths, dung-pits and scratching posts.

Surveys

Wherever development sites include habitat that is suitable for badgers, surveys must be conducted by a suitably-experienced person. See table (pages 34–36) for survey timing.

WHAT IF BADGERS ARE FOUND ON SITE AFTER WORKS HAVE STARTED?

Development sites that include habitat suitable for badgers should have been surveyed and, if necessary, mitigation measures agreed before seeking planning permission.

Even so, badgers will often continue to try to use established paths, despite any obstacles or dangers and may turn up on site even after the start of works. If evidence of badgers is found (or suspected) on site after works have started, works in the area must **stop immediately**. Advice must be sought from an experienced ecologist and the relevant SNCO.

If a sett is discovered during the badger breeding season, ie between 1 December and 30 June, works may have to be suspended until July, when a mitigation can be conducted under licence.

Mitigation measures

- disturbance, exclusion and sett destruction can normally be undertaken only between 1 July and 30 November (and only under licence)

- where a main sett is to be lost, and possibly smaller setts, an alternative sett must be provided, eg an artificial sett

- where artificial setts are required, these will have to be constructed and available at least six months before closure of existing setts and will require an exclusion zone of at least 30 m with no public access. The area around the new sett should be planted up with a thick cover using appropriate native shrubs and trees

- before a sett can be destroyed, badgers must be excluded. Sett closure can take several weeks to complete

- construction works should be started immediately after setts have been destroyed, as time delays may lead to badgers re-excavating old setts.

Mitigation measures may also include:

- maintaining food sources for badgers before and after development

- fencing and provision of badger tunnels or bridges

- traffic calming measures

- post-construction monitoring.

Positive impacts through development

- spoil can be used to create embankments for sett location

- landscaping could include the planting of native fruit and nut-bearing trees for food supply

- recently stripped topsoil can provide areas of short grassland, eg gardens and recreation areas – this will increase the supply of earthworms as food

- adding a raised ledge along one side of a stream culverts may enable badgers (and other species) to use them to cross under roads safely.

Mitigation

- Where impacts are completely unavoidable, mitigation measures will need to be agreed and set in place before works go ahead. Please refer to mitigation section on previous page.

- The timing and methods of mitigation must take other protected species into account.

- Mitigation is likely to take several weeks, if not months, to complete

- Refer to table (pages 34–36) for timing of mitigation.

Guidelines for conducting surveys

- surveys must be undertaken by a specialist

- the best time to conduct surveys for badgers. See table (pages 34–36)

- if required, bait-marking surveys will involve three or more survey days spread over a minimum of three weeks.

Examples of works that require an SNCO badger licence

As a general guide SNCOs advise that a badger licence should be obtained for the following development activities around a badger sett:

- use of heavy machinery (eg tracked vehicles, such as quarry vehicles) within 30 m of any active sett

- use of light machinery (eg wheeled vehicles, such as JCBs) within 20 m of any active sett

- digging or scrub clearance by hand within 10 m of any active sett.

Use of explosives or pile driving are special circumstances that need to be assessed on a case-by-case basis. For example, sheet piling creates a great deal of noise and vibration and may, therefore, require a licence for works to be conducted in the vicinity of a badger sett, even in excess of 30 m.

A badger sett excavated during construction works. The long delays this is likely to cause can be prevented if proper surveys are carried out before work starts.

Badgers will attempt to return to their old setts if they have not been successfully excluded, even once works have started and old setts have been destroyed.

A concrete pipe enables badgers and other species to cross safely under a road.

Setts and territories

Each social group of badgers occupies a territory. Within the territory there may be different types of sett that vary in size and level of usage. All types of sett are legally protected.

The status of territories and setts should be determined by a suitably-experienced person.

Badger territory

- each social group has a defended territory that does not usually overlap with those of neighbouring badger groups

- the size of a territory ranges from 25–150 ha, depending on the quality of food available and the density of badgers in the area

- the edge of a territory is usually within 1 km of the main sett, and is marked by small dung-pits or "latrines". These are also found throughout the territory.

Types of badger sett

- main sett: 3–12 holes or more, with large spoil heaps and a network of obvious badger paths. Most breeding occurs here

- annexe setts: up to eight holes – occur within 150 m of the main sett, connected to it by well-worn paths and may not be in constant use. Second litters of cubs may be reared here.

- subsidiary setts: up to four or five holes 50 m or more away from the main sett – no obvious paths connecting to other setts. Not in continuous use

- outlying setts: 1–3 holes with small spoil heaps and no obvious connecting paths. Used sporadically for resting.

THE BADGER YEAR

Key
Peak numbers
Moderate numbers
Few individuals

Behaviour	J	F	M	A	M	J	J	A	S	O	N	D
Active but mostly below ground	Peak											Peak
Birth of cubs	Moderate	Peak	Moderate	Moderate	Few							Few
Cubs below ground		Peak	Peak	Peak	Moderate							
Adults active above ground		Peak	Peak	Peak	Peak	Peak	Peak	Peak	Peak	Peak	Peak	
Cubs active above ground				Few	Moderate	Peak	Peak	Peak	Peak	Peak	Peak	

Bats

WHAT DO THEY LOOK LIKE?

There are 16 species of bat currently confirmed as resident in the UK (2003).

British bats are very small. They can crawl into holes and crevices of just 15 mm × 20 mm, eg underneath a closed door.

Their bodies are covered in brown-grey fur and they have large, dark, leathery wings which are folded against the body when roosting.

Natural history

Bats roost either individually or in colonies – large colonies can include 200 or more bats.

They feed at night and spend the daytime roosting in buildings, trees, caves etc. They hibernate in winter.

Habitat requirements

Bats are found throughout the British Isles, but individual species vary in their range.

They roost in buildings, bridges, quarries, trees and underground structures, and forage in habitats such as woodland, scrub, parkland, farmland, hedgerows, wetlands and waterways, suburban gardens and well-lit urban open spaces.

Legal protection

Without a development licence, it is illegal to kill, injure or disturb bats or to damage, destroy or obstruct bat roosts (whether occupied or not).

PENALTIES

Depending on the legislation concerned, offences are punishable by fines of up to £5000 per offence (for example, destruction of a single tree that served as a bat roost). Penalties may also include prison sentences of up to six months. In addition, any vehicle used to commit the offence may be forfeited. Either the company and/or individuals may be held liable. Penalties may be higher where dealt with in crown court.

Why do they need special protection?

- bat numbers have declined dramatically over the past 50 years due to the loss of roost sites and feeding habitat, the use of pesticides (eg in timber treatment) and direct persecution

- a report published in 2003 by the RSPB and the Bat Conservation Trust, showed that over a two-year study period 144 offences against bats were committed, with 80 per cent involving damage to roosts. Two thirds of these offences were committed as a result of building and construction works.

Under the *Wildlife and Countryside Act 1981*, the *Wildlife Order (NI) 1985* and the *Habitats Regulations 1994* (and *NI 1995*) it is illegal to:

- intentionally or deliberately kill, injure or capture bats
- intentionally, deliberately or recklessly* disturb bats
- intentionally, deliberately or recklessly* damage, destroy or obstruct any place used for shelter or protection, ie bat roosts (even if they are not currently occupied)
- possess, sell or transport a bat, or anything derived from it.

* In England and Wales the term "recklessly" has been added as an amendment to the *Wildlife and Countryside Act 1981* as a result of the *CRoW Act 2000*. *Nature Conservation (Scotland) Act 2004* strengthens legal protection for bats in Scotland to include "reckless acts".

Bat signs

Bat droppings or stained areas may be found on the ground and on walls around access points or roosting sites.  Bat droppings are brown or black and about three to 10 mm long. They are similar to mouse droppings but bat droppings are softer and drier, and crumble up into a fine powder of shiny insect fragments when crushed.

The legislation applies to both adult and young bats.

Under the *Habitats Regulations 1994* (and *NI 1995*) bat feeding areas receive legal protection where they have been designated as SACs. However, there may also be other, non-designated but important feeding habitats that should be safeguarded from destruction.

What qualifies as a bat roost?

A roost is any structure or place used by bats for shelter or protection. Bats tend to reuse roost sites year after year, and so a roost is protected even if not currently occupied and records from several years ago may still be valid.

Legislation and nature conservation guidance

Bats that have been captured are protected by UK animal welfare legislation, which prohibits cruelty (*Protection of Mammals Act 1996, Welfare of Animals Act 1972 (NI)*. Some species of bat are also listed in the UK BAP.

Licensing for development

Under the **Habitats Regulations 1994** (and **NI 1995**), before any development works that will impact on bats or bat roosts can be carried out, a development licence must be obtained from Defra, SEERAD, the WA or EHS-NH(NI). Applications will require evidence of surveys and mitigation. Licences can take up to 30 days or more to be granted.

Surveys

Wherever development will affect structures or habitat that may be used by bats, surveys must be conducted by a suitably-trained and experienced specialist. Roost inspections can be undertaken only by someone holding a roost visitor licence. For timing of surveys, see table on pages 34–36.

Mitigation

For information on the timing of mitigation, see table on pages 34–36.

- mitigation works may take many weeks or months to complete and in some cases can run into the following year

What if bats are found on site after works have started?

If bats are found after works have started, all works must stop immediately. Consult an experienced ecologist and/or EN, CCW, SNH or EHS-NH (NI).

It will be necessary to undertake surveys and design mitigation measures, and works on roosts may have to be delayed until the appropriate time of year.

Long-eared bat emerging from roost

It is also illegal for anyone other than licensed bat-workers to enter a known bat roost and/or capture and handle bats (exceptions apply to households and injured bats).

- any mitigation measures will normally need to be put in place *before the actual development work can proceed*

- timing of mitigation must take other protected species on site, such as birds, into consideration

- any losses of bat roosts or, in some cases, feeding habitat must be compensated for by the provision of artificial roosts or other suitable structures and/or planting to provide feeding habitat. Artificial roosts must be made available before the destruction of existing roosts

- previous efforts at mitigation have highlighted the importance of maintaining linear features, both during and after construction, as these represent essential flight-lines for certain bat species. This may involve the use of temporary fencing or planting during construction

- works involving tree roosts: tree felling should be conducted only in autumn (or spring if there are no birds breeding) and in the presence of a licensed bat worker, (See Box "Safe working periods" on page 58) and under a Defra licence

- works in buildings: before carrying out any works involving the redevelopment of any building with a bat roost, a development licence must be obtained and advice sought from the SNCO

- use of toxic preservative chemicals for timber treatment etc, and use of pesticides is illegal if it causes harm or damage to bats or their roosts.

Roosting

Every building, structure and mature tree is a potential bat roost!
Bats can crawl into tiny cracks and crevices in the walls, eaves and roofs of buildings.

Some bat species roost inside the roof apex while others prefer to squeeze into small gaps between roof tiles and felt, under barge and soffit boards, in the eaves or in cavity walls.

Bats use different roost sites at different times of year for feeding, mating, giving birth and hibernating.

Summer roost sites include holes and cracks in trees as well as in roofs and walls of buildings.

Winter or hibernation roosts are colder and are usually underground (caves, cellars, tunnels, mines), although trees, buildings and bridges may also be used. The roofs of houses are generally too warm for hibernation, but they may use spaces in the walls.

All old or damaged trees are potential bat roosts.

Other mitigation measures for bats may include:

- creation of artificial roosts (eg bat boxes) or roosting chambers

- construction of bridges and underpasses

- linear planting to provide flight corridors

- careful design of lighting

- post-development monitoring.

A new roost is provided in an artificial bat chamber.

Positive impacts through development

- provision of new roosting opportunities in parts of buildings and other structures

- provision of bat boxes for additional roost sites

- creation of wetlands, rides, greenways and other feeding habitats

- creation or maintenance of hedgerows or rows of trees

- traffic-calming measures and use of low-spill lighting.

Above: a purpose-built bat "hotel" capable of providing roosting space for a large number of bats. Bat boxes can be any shape or size.

Health and safety advice – rabies

- In November 2002, a man died from bat rabies after handling a Dauberton's bat in Scotland. He was the first person for a century to contract and die from this type of rabies in Britain.

- In the whole of continental Europe, bats have passed on the virus to only three people in the last 26 years.

- The only danger is to those people who handle bats – apart from members of the public who may handle injured animals, only licensed bat specialists are allowed to handle bats.

- Bat workers are advised to have a rabies vaccination and wear gloves.

- See Defra and BCT websites.

Safe working periods for bat roosts (following appropriate mitigation and licensing)

Work on roosts can be undertaken only when bats are absent. *The following table is a guide only* – exact timing will vary with geographic location and weather conditions. *For all cases where works will impact on bats and/or bat roosts, advice about the timing of works must be obtained on a case-by-case basis from a suitably experienced person.*

	Key
	Unsafe to proceed without thorough investigation – **roost very likely to be occupied**
	Proceed with caution – **roost may be occupied**. *Seek advice if bats are found!*
	Relatively safe period to work – **roost unlikely to be occupied**. *Seek advice if bats are found!*
	Safest period to work – **Bats least vulnerable** (ie not hibernating or breeding)

Roost type	J	F	M	A	M	J	J	A	S	O	N	D
Hibernation roosts												
Maternity roosts												
Potential roosts: type unknown												
Bats least vulnerable												

* Timing may differ for tree roosts in that it may be possible for trees to be felled from January to March and in November and December in cases where clearance is required before the bird-nesting season. However, *all trees must be checked for bats* by a suitably-experienced person *before felling*.

** Swarming around roosts may occur at this time of year. Stop all works if bats are present.

THE BAT YEAR

	Key
	Peak numbers
	Moderate numbers
	Few individuals

Behaviour	J	F	M	A	M	J	J	A	S	O	N	D
In hibernation roosts												
Adults active and feeding												
Females and young in maternity roosts												
Mating season												

CIRIA C567

Birds

WHAT DO WE NEED TO KNOW ABOUT BIRDS?

Legal protection

All wild birds (ie resident, visiting and introduced species) in the UK are protected by law under the *Wildlife and Countryside (WCA) Act 1981 (as amended),* the *Wildlife (NI) Order 1985,* and the *Wildlife and Countryside (Amendment (Scotland)) Regulations 2001,* making it illegal to:

- kill, injure or take any wild bird

- take, damage or destroy the nest of any wild bird while it is being built or in use

- take or destroy the eggs of any wild bird

- possess or control (eg for exhibition or sale) any wild bird or egg unless obtained legally.

Wild birds that are found injured may be captured or humanely killed.

Birds that receive special protection

Species listed in *Schedule 1* of the *WCA 1981* and the *Wildlife Order (NI) 1985* (see table p65) receive special protection. In addition to the above offences, it is also illegal to intentionally or recklessly* disturb any bird listed on Schedule 1 while nesting, or at or to disturb any of its dependent young. Disturbance could occur, for example, through noise caused by construction works in close proximity to the nest.

* The term "recklessly" applies in England and Wales following the *CRoW Act 2000,* and in Scotland following the *Nature Conservation (Scotland) Act 2004.*

Other legislation and nature conservation guidance

- refer to Appendix (Legislation tables p180) for details of designation of Special Protected Areas (SPA) for birds. The SNCO must be consulted whenever works may impact on an SPA.

Birds are protected against cruelty under the **Protection of Animals Act 1911** and the **Welfare of Animals Act 1972 (NI)**.

Many bird species are now included in the *UK Biodiversity Action Plan*.

Barn owl

Licensing for development

There is no provision for SNCOs to issue licences for development works that impact on birds. To avoid prosecution, it must be shown that all reasonable effort was made to avoid breaking the law. This requires adequate surveys and mitigation plans before undertaking any works that will impact on birds. EN, SNH, CCW or EHS-NH(NI) should be consulted.

Peregrine falcon

Surveys and mitigation

Wherever development impacts on structures or habitat that may be used by nesting birds (in reality, most places), surveys should be conducted by a suitably experienced person.

WHAT IF BREEDING BIRDS ARE FOUND ON SITE AFTER WORKS HAVE STARTED?

Black redstart

- if nesting birds are found on site, then all works in that area will have to stop – maybe for a month or more depending on the species – until the birds have completed breeding and young birds have left the nest

- during the breeding season, suspected nesting sites should be inspected only by experienced ecologists

Kingfisher

- birds often move onto construction sites to nest on machinery, such as cranes, or piles of debris and temporary site structures. If this occurs the machinery or other structures will not be able to be used until the birds have completed nesting, and areas may need to be sealed off to prevent disturbance.

Although the majority of birds breed during spring and summer, they can be found breeding on site at unexpected times of year. It is advisable to check machinery, stockpiles and temporary structures on a regular basis, to avoid breaking the law.

Mitigation for birds

*British bird species given special protection under **Schedule 1 of the WCA 1981 and the Wildlife Order 1985**: it is illegal to disturb these birds while they are nesting.*

SCHEDULE 1, PART I

SCHEDULE 1, PART II (most species are protected between 1 February and 31 August

Protected in: England, Wales and Scotland only		Northern Ireland only	All UK
Avocet	Black redstart	Corn bunting *	Bittern *
Bee-eater	Redwing	Common buzzard	Chough
Bittern, little	Scarlet rosefinch	Turtle dove *	Corncrake *
Bluethroat	Green sandpiper	Dunlin	Common crossbill
Brambling	Purple sandpiper	Pied flycatcher	Red-throated diver
Cirl bunting *	Wood sandpiper	Goosander	Dotterel
Lapland bunting	Scaup	Sparrow hawk	Golden eagle
Snow bunting	Velvet scoter	Grey heron	White-tailed eagle
Honey buzzard	Serin	Kestrel	Peregrine falcon
Spotted crake	Shorelark	Nightjar	Fieldfare
Crossbills (all) *(Scottish)	Red-backed shrike *	Ring ousel	Firecrest
Stone curlew *	Spoonbill	Long-eared owl	Garganey
Divers (all)	Black-winged stilt	Short-eared owl	Black-tailed godwit
Long-tailed duck	Temminck's stilt	Storm petrel	Goshawk
Gyr falcon	Black tern	Tree pipit	Black-necked grebe
Slavonian grebe	Crested tit	Common redstart	Greenshank
Little gull	Short-toed tree-creeper	Arctic tern	Hen harrier *
Mediterranean gull	Cetti's warbler	Common tern	Marsh harrier
Harriers (all)	Dartford warbler	Sandwich tern	Kingfisher
Purple heron	Marsh warbler	Twite	Merlin
Hobby	Savi's warbler *	Yellow wagtails	Osprey
Hoopoe	Woodlark *	Reed warbler	Barn owl
Red kite	Wryneck *	Wood warbler	Red-necked phalarope *
Golden oriole	Greylag goose (ltd. areas)	Garden warbler	Common quail *
Wryneck *		Gadwall	Ruff
Snowy owl	Protected in Scotland only:	Golden plover	Common scoter *
Leach's petrel		Pochard	Bewick's swan
Kentish plover	Capercaillie	Scaup	Whooper swan
Little-ringed plover		Shoveler	Little tern
		Wigeon	Roseate tern *
			Bearded tit
			Whimbrel
			Goldeneye
			Pintail

Mitigation measures for birds may include re-scheduling of works to avoid breeding times or, if this is not possible, setting up exclusion areas around nesting birds by erecting wooden or plastic screening to reduce noise and visual disturbance.

There is no blanket guidance for the amount of space surrounding the nest that must be left undisturbed. This will vary according to species and location. Consult a specialist.

Mitigation measures may include:

- construction of buildings with ledges, access slots underneath eaves etc, for nesting
- planting of trees, shrubs etc to provide new nesting and feeding habitat
- buildings with green roofs – these provide feeding habitat for birds
- provision of nest boxes (including brick boxes) and water baths.

Black-tailed godwit

Works affecting birds

All operations that will impact on areas or structures that are being used by nesting birds must be conducted, where possible, between August and February only (ie outside of the bird breeding season). This includes:

- clearance of scrub and trees
- mowing or strimming of areas likely to be used by ground-nesting species
- building demolition or maintenance.

Individual species may still be breeding at this time. If breeding birds are found, stop all works and consult an ecologist.

Works cannot be conducted near to nesting *Schedule 1* species, as this would lead to disturbance.

Birds are likely to occur on most sites – scrub clearance should be conducted outside the bird nesting season wherever possible. If this is not feasible, a watching brief for birds nesting must be implemented by an experienced ecologist. The timing of vegetation clearance must take other protected species on site into consideration (eg bats, reptiles or great crested newts).

Nest location:	Examples of species that may occur
Tree holes and crevices in walls	Blue tit, great tit, house sparrow, jackdaw, kestrel, little owl, robin, swift, starling
Buildings (ledges, eaves etc)	Black redstart, blackbird, peregrine falcon, kestrel, little owl, pigeon, robin, swift, song thrush, swallow, house martin
Under eaves, under bridges, caves	House martin, swift, pied wagtail
Barns, ruins, churches, old buildings	Barn owl, tawny owl, swallow, kestrel
Cliff and quarry faces and crevices	Barn owl, jackdaw, peregrine falcon, kestrel, little owl, swift, sand martin
Hedgerow, bramble, bushes, trees	Bullfinch, chaffinch, goldfinch, greenfinch
Ground	Corn bunting, lapwing, partridge, skylark, yellowhammer
Sandpit, burrows	Little owl, tawny owl, sand martin colonies, kingfisher in river banks
Woodpiles	Hedge sparrow, wren
Rushes, grass	Black-headed gulls (usually on islands) and on the ground, red bunting and sedge warbler
Parks, river banks, ponds, reservoirs	Coot, mallard, moorhen, swan
Temporary structures on construction sites (cranes, scaffolding, stock piles etc	Crows, pigeons, sand martins, pied wagtail

Where to go for further help and guidance

Organisations that can be contacted for expert advice on birds:

- SNCOs
- RSPB
- British Trust for Ornithology
- wildlife trusts

Surveys:

- times at which surveys and mitigation can be conducted are restricted – to avoid expensive time delays, surveys must be undertaken several months before works are due to start

- surveys for breeding birds must be undertaken between March and July, with at least some visits conducted during the peak months of May and June

- surveys for over-wintering birds are conducted between September and March, with at least some surveys conducted in September/October and March.

Licences to control certain bird species

Certain species are recognised as having the potential to cause problems. These are:

- carrion crow
- Canada goose
- collared dove
- great black-backed gull
- lesser black-backed gull
- herring gull
- jackdaw
- jay
- magpie
- feral pigeon
- rook
- wood pigeon

Defra, SEERAD, EHS-NH (NI) and the WA issue a number of general licences, which allow authorised persons (ie land owner or occupier) to kill or take the above species using certain methods.

In some instances, it may be legal under a general licence to carry out specific control measures that are usually prohibited, for example killing or taking of birds or destruction of nests. Only certain methods of control are permissible under the general licence. For example the use of stupefying bait, mist nets and carbon dioxide are not permitted.

Before undertaking any control measures it must be shown that control was necessary for any of the following reasons:

- preventing the spread of disease
- to preserve public health, or public or air safety
- preventing serious damage to livestock, foodstuffs for livestock, crops, vegetables, fruits, growing timber, fisheries or inland waters.

It is not legal to kill or control these species just because they are a nuisance, noisy or inconvenient etc. These problems can be controlled using non-lethal methods only, such as bird-scarers or proofing to prevent access.

General licences are issued as general dispensations and, as such, a licence application is not usually necessary. However, to avoid breaking the law, a copy of the general licence should be obtained and read, and advice should be sought from a professional pest controller, and Defra, SEERAD, the WA, or EHS-NH (NI), before undertaking any control measures.

Where problems cannot be resolved by actions permitted under the general licence and there is no other solution, an application for an individual licence should be made to Defra, SEERAD, EHS-NH(NI) or the WA for permission to use prohibited methods of control.

It is illegal for any control measures to impact on other protected species, for example bats or bat roosts.

Common mammals

WHAT DO WE NEED TO KNOW ABOUT COMMON MAMMALS?

In addition to the protected species that are dealt with elsewhere in this guidance, a number of mammal species that have limited legal protection may be found on construction sites.

Though presence of these species does not limit development works, care should be taken to protect and remove individuals from danger by following the guidance provided below.

Many of these species are of conservation concern, primarily through habitat loss, and further damage to their populations should be avoided wherever possible.

Legislation and nature conservation guidance

All mammals in Britain are protected against cruelty by the *Wild Mammals (Protection) Act, 1996* and the *Welfare of Animals Act (NI) 1972*.

Hedgehogs, shrews and polecats

Hedgehogs, all shrew species and polecats are protected against the use of certain methods of killing or trapping under the *Wildlife and Countryside Act 1981*. In Northern Ireland, the hedgehog receives the same protection under the **Wildlife Order 1985**. This makes all trapping illegal unless done under licence.

Identifying common mammals

Hedgehog (*Erinaceus europaeus*)

Description: Small nocturnal insect-eating mammal with a pig-like snout and a coat of spines; rolls itself up for defence.

Size: Up to 275 mm plus short tail.

Breeding: May to October

Distribution: Recorded throughout the UK.

Conservation status: Listed as priority species under the *UK Biodiversity Action Plan.*

Common shrew (*Sorex cireneus*)

Description: Common shrews have silky dark brown fur, with a pale underside and light brown flanks. Long pointed snout and small eyes.

Size: Up to 87 mm plus long tail.

Breeding: April to August

Distribution: Recorded in England, Wales and Scotland only

Conservation status: UK's second most common mammal.

Stoats, weasels, voles, mice and moles

Not legally protected in the United Kingdom (apart from under the **Wild Mammals Act 1996** and the **Welfare of Animals Act (NI) 1972**.

Hares and rabbits

Brown and mountain hares have additional legal protection through the **Ground Game Act 1880**, the **Hare Preservation Act 1892** and the **Protection of Animals Act 1911**. They may not be offered for sale between 1 March and 31 July, to discourage shooting during the main breeding season.

Landowners are required to prevent rabbits from damaging neighbours' land by taking appropriate control measures.

Practical measures for dealing with these species on construction sites

Before conducting works on any habitat, seek expert advice about the suitability of habitat for protected species, and conduct surveys where appropriate.

Even if no protected species are confirmed to be present, destruction of habitat should be avoided wherever possible.

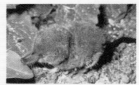

Pygmy shrew (*Sorex minutus*)

Description: Silky brown fur, with a pale underside. Long pointed snout, small eyes and hardly visible ears.

Size: Up to 64 mm plus long tail.

Breeding: April to August

Distribution: Recorded throughout the UK.

Conservation status: Included within local biodiversity action plans.

Water shrew (*Neomys fodiens*)

Description: The largest of the British shrews: short, dense, velvety and jet black fur on the upper surface of the body, usually greyish white or yellowish underneath. Long pointed snout, small ears and tiny eyes.

Size: Up to 96 mm plus tail.

Breeding: April to September

Distribution: Recorded in England, Wales and Scotland only.

Conservation status: Identified as a species of conservation concern by the UK Biodiversity Steering Group and included within some local biodiversity action plans.

Where clearance of vegetation is required, care should be taken, if practical, to avoid killing or injuring small mammals which are particularly vulnerable if they are nocturnal, hibernating or breeding. Protect and remove all individuals from danger and watch out for nests of young amongst long grass or scrub. Young are born blind, without fur and are highly vulnerable.

Special care must be taken when clearance is carried out in winter, when many species are hibernating under-ground and are vulnerable to injury and to predation if left exposed.

If in any doubt about the identification of the species you have found, stop all works immediately. Several mammal species receive strict legal protection. Consult an expert to avoid breaking the law.

Stoat (*Mustela erminea*)

Description: Long slender body with short legs. Medium-short tail (length 95–140 mm) always with a black tip. Fur reddish brown to ginger above, white to cream below.

Size: Up to 310 mm plus tail.

Breeding: April to July

Distribution: Recorded throughout the UK.

Conservation status: Common and widespread.

Weasel (*Mustela nivalis*)

Description: Fur ginger to russet brown, cream below. Long slender body, short tail.

Size: Up to 314 mm plus tail.

Breeding: April to August

Distribution: Recorded in England, Wales and Scotland only.

Conservation status: common and widespread.

Polecat (*Mustela putorius*)

Description: Fur dark brown with large white patches on nose, cheeks and around edge of ears; long slender body with short legs and tail.

Size: Up to 460 mm plus tail.

Breeding: March to July

Distribution: Recorded in England, Wales and Scotland only.

Conservation status: Listed as a species of conservation concern by the UK Biodiversity Steering Group.

Short-tailed field vole (*Microtus agrestis*)

Description: Fur long and brownish grey with grey underside. Rounded body with a blunt nose and short tail.

Size: Up to 135 mm plus short tail.

Breeding: April to September, or all year round.

Distribution: Recorded in England, Wales and Scotland only

Conservation status: Locally common.

Bank vole (*Clethrionomys glareolus*)

Description: Fur reddish with grey sides; rounded body, blunt nose and long tail.

Size: Up to 110 mm plus long tail.

Breeding: Usually April to October, but can breed all year round.

Distribution: Recorded in England, Wales and Scotland only (June 2003).

Conservation status: Common.

Brown hare/Irish hare (*Lepus europaeus*)

Description: Similar to rabbit, but very long legs and longer, black-tipped ears.

Size: Up to 700 mm plus short tail.

Breeding: February to October

Distribution: Recorded throughout the UK.

Conservation status: Listed as a priority species under the *UK Biodiversity Action Plan.*

Rabbit (*Oryctolagus cuniculus*)

Description: Fur brown/grey/black. Long hind legs, long ears without black-tips, short tail that is white underneath.

Size: Up to 500 mm plus tail.

Breeding: February to October

Distribution: Recorded throughout the UK.

Conservation status: Widespread. Grazing by rabbits can be very beneficial to maintain diversity of habitats, such as chalk grassland, heathland and sand dunes.

Harvest mouse (*Micromys minutus*)

Description: Smallest UK rodent. Fur red above, white underside. Blunt nose and long tail.

Size: Up to 80 mm plus long tail.

Breeding: May to October/December

Distribution: Recorded in England, Wales and Scotland only.

Conservation status: Subject to national and local biodiversity action plans.

Wood mouse (*Apodemus sylvaticus*)

Description: Fur dark brown with yellow-brown sides and grey-white underside. Narrow, yellow collar. Pointed nose, large ears, eyes and hind-feet and long tail.

Size: Up to 103 mm plus tail.

Breeding: March to October (occasionally throughout year)

Distribution: Recorded throughout the UK.

Conservation status: The most common wild rodent.

Yellow-necked mouse (*Apodemus flavicollis*)

Description: Similar to wood mouse but yellow patch on throat and richer brown fur with purer white underside. Pointed nose, large ears, eyes and hind-feet and long tail.

Size: Up to 130 mm plus long tail.

Breeding: April to October

Distribution: Recorded in England, Wales and Scotland only.

Conservation status: Included under national and local biodiversity action plans.

House mouse (*Mus musculus*)

Description: Fur uniform grey-brown with slightly lighter undersides. Pointed nose, large ears, eyes and long tail

Size: Up to 103 mm plus tail.

Breeding: All year round

Distribution: Recorded throughout the UK.

Conservation status: Common and widespread, particularly in urban areas.

Mole (*Talpa europaea*)

Description: Short black velvety fur. Long, cylindrical body, broad feet with large claws; front feel spade-like. Tiny eyes and bright pink fleshy nose.

Size: Approximately 143 mm plus short tail.

Breeding: May to June

Distribution: Recorded in England, Wales and Scotland only (June 2003).

Conservation status: Common and widespread.

Deer

There are six species of deer found wild in the UK: red deer, roe deer, fallow deer, Chinese water deer, Sika deer and muntjac deer (see descriptions on page 77). Only two of these, red deer and roe deer are native to the UK. All others have been introduced and are becoming increasingly widespread.

Legislation and nature conservation guidance

Under the **Deer Act 1991** and **Deer (Scotland) Act 1996** all wild deer (except muntjac and Chinese water deer) are protected against killing and taking by a close season (the timing of which varies between species). Fallow, red and sika deer receive similar protection under the **Wildlife (NI) Order 1985**.

Killing of deer at night and the use of certain methods of taking and killing are also prohibited under this legislation. These activities can be licenced by EN, CCW, SNH or EHS in order to remove deer from one area to another or for taking deer alive for scientific or education purposes.

Under the **Wildlife and Countryside Act 1981 (as amended)** it is illegal to release non-native species. This includes muntjac and sika deer.

Chinese water deer (Hydropetes inermis)

Description: Reddish brown in the summer, turning sandy brown in the winter. No antlers.

Size: up to 55 cm at the shoulder

Breeding: November until April.

Distribution: Bedfordshire, Cambridgeshire, Suffolk and Norfolk.

Conservation status: Introduced, IUCN Red Data book Listed as "lower risk, near threatened" in China, the UK holds 10 per cent of the world population.

Fallow deer (Dama dama)

Description: Can be highly variable in colour from black to white, in general have a chestnut summer coat with white/cream spots, in winter are grey/brown with spots indistinct or absent. Males have antlers growing up to 70 cm long

Size: up to 1 m at the shoulder.

Distribution: patchy in Scotland, also found in north-east England, the Midlands, southern England and north and east Wales.

Breeding: September to February

Conservation status: Naturalised, locally abundant and increasing.

Muntjac deer (Muntiacus reevesi)

Size: Grow up to 52 cm at the shoulder.

Description: In summer are reddish brown, turning grey-brown in the winter. Males' antlers are short, growing up to only 10 cm.

Distribution: Found in south and central England and Wales, further north distribution is patchy, but almost reaches the Scottish border.

Breeding: All year round.

Conservation status: Introduced, widespread and increasing in number and range.

Red deer (Cervus elaphus)

Description: Reddish brown summer coat, brown/grey winter coat. Male has large, highly branched antlers

Size: UK's largest land mammals, up to 137 cm at the shoulder

Breeding: End of September to November.

Distribution: Native stock is common in the Scottish Highlands, Dumfriesshire, Lake District, East Anglia and the south-west of England. Feral stock is present in the north of England, north Midlands, East Anglia, the New Forest and Sussex.

Conservation status: Native, widespread and common.

Roe deer (Capreolus carpreolus)

Description: Foxy red in the summer, turning grey, pale brown and occasionally black in the winter. The males have short antlers (<30 cm).

Size: Up to 75 cm at the shoulder

Breeding: Mid-July to mid-August.

Distribution: Found throughout Scotland and England, except parts of Kent and the Midlands, invading Wales from England.

Conservation status: Native, widespread and common.

Sika deer (Cervus nippon)

Description: In summer are reddish brown to yellowish brown, with dark dorsal stripe surrounded by white spots. In winter are dark grey to black and spots are faint or absent. Males have branched antlers.

Size: Grow up to 95 cm at the shoulder

Breeding: End of September to November.

Distribution: Patchy, includes northern and western Scotland, Kintyre, Peebles-shire, Lake District, Lancashire, Northamptonshire, Bedfordshire, New Forest, Dorset, County Fermanagh and County Tyrone.

Conservation status: Introduced, locally abundant and increasing.

Dormouse

IDENTIFYING DORMICE

What do they look like?

- the most dominant features of the dormouse, also referred to as the hazel dormouse (*Muscardinus avellanarius*), are its large black eyes, the orange-brown coat and thickly furred tail. Young dormice are greyer

- the fat (or "edible") dormouse (*Glis glis*) is an introduced species found in central and southern England. It is grey and larger in size

- always consult an expert to confirm which species of dormouse you have found.

Without a development licence, it is illegal to kill, injure, capture or disturb dormice, or to damage or obstruct places used for shelter, protection, resting or breeding.

- mitigation works may take many weeks or months to complete; any mitigation measures will normally need to be put in place before the actual development work can proceed.

- the timing of mitigation must take other protected species that occur on the site into consideration – for example, clearance of vegetation may affect bats, reptiles and nesting birds.

PENALTIES

Offences are punishable by fines of up to £5000 per offence (for example, reckless destruction of a section of hedge that contains a nest with young dormice). Penalties may also include prison sentences of up to six months. In addition, any vehicle used to commit the offence may be forfeited. Either the company and/or individuals may be held liable. Penalties may be higher where dealt with in crown court.

Natural history

- the dormouse is a solitary and nocturnal animal and spends most of its time above ground level in trees and shrubs, except in hibernation when nests may be found at or below ground level.

Habitat requirements

- dormice can occur throughout England and Wales, but are concentrated in Wales and central and southern England, with isolated populations in some northern counties

- they live mostly in woodland and thick hedges, but they may also be found in areas of bracken and scrub

- nests are all made of grasses and leaves, and are found among tangled vegetation, in hedgerows and tree holes and, sometimes, buildings

- winter hibernation nests are often at ground level under leaf litter, woodpiles, rocks etc.

What do we need to know about dormice?

Legal protection

Dormice and their habitat are fully protected under the **Wildlife and Countryside Act 1981 (as amended)** and the **Habitats Regulations 1994,** making it illegal to:

- intentionally or deliberately kill, injure or capture dormice

- intentionally, deliberately or recklessly* disturb dormice

- intentionally, deliberately or recklessly* damage, destroy or obstruct breeding or resting sites or places used for shelter or protection (whether occupied or not)

- possess or transport a dormouse (or any part thereof) unless under licence

- sell or exchange dormice.

* For England and Wales the term "reckless" was added as an amendment to the Wildlife and Countryside Act as a result of the CRoW Act 2000.

The legislation applies to both adult and juvenile dormice.

Other legislation and nature conservation guidance

Dormice are protected against cruelty under the **Protection of Mammals Act 1996**.

The dormouse is a priority species under the *UK Biodiversity Action Plan* (BAP).

Licensing for development

Before conducting any development or mitigation works that will affect dormice or their habitat, a development licence must first be obtained from Defra or the

WA. These will be granted only to a suitably-qualified ecologist and will depend on evidence of adequate surveys and mitigation plans. Licences can take 30 days or more to be granted.

Surveys

Wherever development will impact on habitat that may be used by dormice for shelter, protection, resting or breeding, surveys must be conducted by a suitably-experienced person. See table on pages 34–36 for survey timetable.

WHAT IF DORMICE ARE FOUND ON SITE AFTER WORKS HAVE STARTED?

If any evidence of dormice being present on site is found after works have started, works in the area must **stop immediately**. Always consult an expert. Works may need to be delayed until licences can be obtained for mitigation to be conducted at the appropriate time of year.

Mitigation for dormice

If impacts on dormice or their habitat cannot be avoided, mitigation will be required. All mitigation proposals must be agreed with the relevant SNCO, and a development licence obtained where required. Methods may include:

1 **Clearance** – this is undertaken in order to encourage dormice to leave an area naturally. Clearance work can be conducted only during two periods in dormouse habitat: either during May, or (preferably) September to early October. Vegetation should be cleared by hand where possible, and a licensed ecologist must be present at all times and a Defra or WA licence will be needed.

    • before clearance, a licensed ecologist must check the litter, moss, bore or tree holes and hedgerow bases for dormice and nests

    • cut vegetation should be chipped or manually taken to areas of no value to dormice. Old hazel stools and honeysuckle should ideally be translocated and replanted

    • temporary removal of vegetation during construction, even if only for the short-term, should be accompanied, preferably, by new planting in safe areas to limit damage to dormouse populations.

Mitigation may also include:

2 **Planting** – to increase habitat area and connectivity.

3 *Nest boxes.*

4 **Green bridges** and/or aerial route-ways.

5 **Post-development management** and monitoring.

6 **Installing wooden gates** in field entrances or covering the top of metal gates with hessian (to enable dormice to cross).

7 **Connecting isolated fragments of woodland** and hedgerow through linear planting along roadsides and within the development

Translocation of dormice is an extremely lengthy and expensive process, requires *at least 20 ha* of suitable habitat in which to re-locate the animals and has limited success; it should be used *only as a last resort.*

Why do they need special protection?
- dormice have undergone a rapid decline in numbers over the last 30 years, and are now extinct in 50 per cent of their range in the UK

- dormice are extremely vulnerable to isolation through, for instance, hedgerow removal, as they are reluctant to cross even small open areas.

Dormouse signs
- include hairs, nibbled hazelnuts and nests woven out of grasses and leaves; nests are 90–150 mm in diameter and may be found among vegetation either above or at ground level.

Dormouse mitigation timetable		
Date of clearance works	Survey and dormouse capture	Survey and capture for translocation (if all habitat to be lost)
May	May – September of previous year	April of previous year to April in year of works
September	May – September of previous year	August of previous year to August in year of works

Where to go for further help and guidance
Organisations that can be contacted for expert advice on dormice:

- SNCOs
- wildlife trusts
- The Mammal Society

A dormouse box can help to replace lost nesting places.

THE DORMOUSE YEAR

	Key
	Peak numbers
	Moderate numbers
	Few individuals

Activity	J	F	M	A	M	J	J	A	S	O	N	D
Hibernation												
Adults active												
Females pregnant												
Birth of young												
Young dependant on female												

Fish

LEGAL PROTECTION

Fish are covered under several pieces of legislation in the UK, as summarised below.

■ *Salmon and Freshwater Fisheries Act 1975, Foyle Fisheries Act (NI) 1952, Fisheries Act (NI) 1966* and *Salmon and Freshwater Fisheries (Consolidation) (Scotland) Act 2003* – this legislation makes it illegal to *poison or injure fish, their spawning grounds, spawn or food of fish* by polluting water, and to fish for or take salmon (including removing them during works or for survey), and in certain cases freshwater fish, without legal right or written permission, or a licence issued for the purpose.

■ Under *Section 30* of the *Salmon and Freshwater Fisheries Act 1975,* a written consent must be obtained from the EA, SEPA or EHS-EP (NI) if fish or spawn are to be introduced into any inland water.

It is illegal to poison or injure fish, their spawning grounds, spawn or food of fish by polluting water; and to fish for or capture salmon.

It is illegal to pollute "controlled waters" such as rivers, lakes, streams, canals, ground-waters, coastal and territorial waters.

It is illegal to kill, injure or disturb certain fish species, or destroy or obstruct certain parts of their habitat.

It is illegal to introduce fish or spawn into an inland water (eg through stream diversion) without written consent from the EA, SEPA or EHS-EP(NI)

■ *Water Resources Act 1991, Controlled Waters (Lakes and Ponds) Order 1989* and *Control of Pollution Act 1974* – this legislation makes it an offence to pollute "controlled waters". Pollution involves permitting "*poisonous, noxious or polluting matter or any solid waste matter*" to enter any such controlled waters. It is also illegal to undertake actions that lead to freshwaters being polluted with cut vegetation, as this can lead to changes to the nutrient status.

- *The Wildlife and Countryside Act 1981 (WCA) (as amended)* protects certain fish species and parts of their habitat in England, Wales and Scotland (See box on page 87 for details).

- *Habitats Regulations 1994 and (NI) 1995* – these protect a number of fish species (See box on page 87 for details).

Fish do not receive protection under the *Wildlife Order 1985* in Northern Ireland and only receive limited protection under the *Habitats Regulations (NI) 1995* as described above.

Conservation guidance

A wide range of freshwater or marine fish species are listed under the *UK Biodiversity Action Plan* (BAP).

Licensing for development

The EA, SEPA or EHS-EP should be consulted before any works on watercourses are carried out. Works on "controlled waters" will require consent from the relevant authority.

Why do they need special protection?

- The pollution of water courses by run-off and sedimentation has led to declines in fish habitat and fish populations.

- Carrying out activities affecting water courses at the wrong time of year leads to damage to breeding populations.

- Changes to river channels can obstruct migration routes to spawning grounds.

- Introduction of fish needs to be controlled to avoid negative impacts on fresh-water ecosystems.

See box "Surveys, licensing and mitigation" on page 86.

There is no provision for SNCOs to issue licences permitting development works affecting fish species protected under the *Wildlife and Countryside Act 1981 only*. To avoid prosecution, it must be shown that all reasonable effort was made to avoid breaking the law.

Where development works are likely to contravene the *Habitats Regulations 1994* or *1995 (NI)*, a development licence must be obtained from Defra, SEERAD, EHS-NH(NI) or the WA.

SURVEYS AND MITIGATION

Survey methods

Surveys to establish fish presence can be conducted at any time of year. Exceptions may apply to migratory species, where surveys for adults would need to coincide with the breeding season. However, where young life-stages are present throughout the year, general surveys to establish presence can still be carried out.

Survey methods that may be used include:

- netting/trawling
- fish traps
- electro-fishing
- electronic tagging of fish (eg to monitor their movements and how they use different habitat areas).

In Scotland, where salmon or freshwater fish are to be taken in any survey, detailed guidance must be sought from SEERAD, as permission or licences may be required.

WHAT IF PROTECTED SPECIES ARE FOUND ON SITE AFTER WORKS HAVE STARTED?

If any protected species of fish are found or suspected on site after works have started, **works in the area must stop immediately**, as it is illegal to injure, kill, capture or disturb any fully-protected species of fish, or to damage its sheltering place. Advice must be sought from an experienced person and the relevant SNCO. Works may have to be delayed until the appropriate time of year for surveying and mitigation.

Mitigation for protected fish on construction sites

If protected fish species are found and impacts on them cannot be avoided, mitigation measures must be agreed with the relevant authority. The type and scale of mitigation will depend on the level of impact.

Mitigation measures may include:

- zoned work areas and buffer zones

- trapping and translocation

- scheduling of works so as to avoid breeding seasons

- creation of "fish ladders" on rivers to prevent interruption of migration routes

- post-construction monitoring of water quality and fish populations.

The EA, SEPA or EHS-EP (NI) must be consulted for expert guidance before carrying out any of the above.

In Scotland, where salmon or freshwater fish are to be taken in any survey, detailed guidance must be sought from SEERAD, as permission or licences may be required.

Breeding season for protected fish species

In some cases it may be necessary to conduct survey during the breeding season. The timing of the breeding season varies among species as follows:

- Allis shad: spring–summer
- Giant goby: spring–summer
- Sturgeon: February–June
- Twaite shad: spring–summer
- Basking shark: summer months
- Vendace: November–January
- Couch's goby: spring–summer
- Whitefish: December–March

Fish species listed on Schedule 5 of the *Wildlife and Countryside Act 1981 (as amended)*

With regard to the species below (unless otherwise stated) under Section 9 of the WCA it is illegal to:

(i) intentionally kill, injure or take these fish species

(ii) intentionally or recklessly* damage, destroy or obstruct places used for shelter or protection

(iii) intentionally or recklessly* disturb these fish species (sheltering or not)

(iv) sell, offer for sale, possess or transport these species (or any part thereof) unless under licence

(v) advertise for buying or selling.

* **For England and Wales the term "reckless" was added under the Countryside and Rights of Way Act 2000.**

- Twaite shad (protected against (iii) only).
- Allis shad (protected against (ii) and (iii) only).
- Giant goby
- Couch's goby
- Whitefish
- Vendace
- Burbot *(this species is now extinct in the UK, though re-introduction programmes are currently being considered)*
- Sturgeon
- Basking shark (also protected against reckless disturbance in ANY place.

Fish species listed under the *Habitats Regulations* 1994 (not NI)

The sturgeon is protected under ***Schedule 2*** against *killing, capture, injury and disturbance*, and its *breeding and resting* sites are protected against *damage, destruction or obstruction.*

Atlantic sturgeon

Protected under the *Habitat Regulations* 1994 and 1995 (NI) against certain methods of killing or capture:

- Atlantic salmon
- River lamprey
- Barbel*
- Grayling*
- Allis shad
- Whitefish*
- Vendace*
- Twaite shad

* England, Wales and Scotland only.

Surveys, licensing and mitigation

To enable appropriate time-tabling of development the following points should be considered:

- surveys should be undertaken whenever works will impact on a watercourse (of any size), including management, improvement or maintenance works such as vegetation management or refurbishment of small bridges and culverts. (See table on pages 34–36.)

- surveys must be undertaken only by people who are suitably-trained and experienced in recognising protected fish species

- consents or licences may be required, in particular if survey methods involve protected species of fish being captured, handled, or disturbed

- fish may also be affected where construction projects impact on fisheries, and advice on any measures to be taken should be sought from the relevant authorities

- where protected fish species are shown to be present, SNCOs require that impacts are avoided where at all possible. Where impacts are completely unavoidable, mitigation measures will need to be agreed and set in place before works go ahead. The timing of mitigation works may be restricted, for instance it may be required to conduct works outside the relevant species' breeding season. (See table on pages 34–36.)

- licences are not granted for works affecting species listed under the WCA 1981 only. To avoid prosecution under the *Wildlife and Countryside Act 1981 (as amended)*, wherever works will impact on protected fish species there must be evidence that every reasonable effort was made to avoid breaking the law – including proof of adequate surveys and mitigation plans. Mitigation measures should be agreed with the EA, SEERAD, SEPA or the relevant SNCO

- to avoid prosecution under the *Habitats Regulations 1994*, wherever works will impact on sturgeon a development licence must be obtained before starting any works. Applications must include evidence of adequate surveys and plans for mitigation, which must be agreed with the EA, SEPA, SEERAD and/or the relevant SNCO. Licences can take up to 30 days or more to be granted

- a licence may be required in Scotland, for works affecting salmon and other freshwater fish – contact SEERAD.

FISH – NATURAL HISTORY AND HABITAT REQUIREMENTS

Habitat requirements

Protected fish species that may be affected by development
are found in the following habitats

Fish species	Habitats in which they are likely to occur
Allis shad	rivers and estuaries, possibly inland lakes
Sturgeon	fast-flowing rivers and estuaries (only a vagrant in the UK)
Couch's goby	inshore and intertidal on sheltered shorelines
Giant goby	inshore and intertidal along rocky shorelines, tidal pools
Twaite shad	inland lakes, rivers and estuaries
Basking shark	warm coastal and cool temperature waters, often straying in-shore. migrate and overwinter in deeper waters
Vendace	inland lakes with gravel substrate (only known at four sites in UK)
Whitefish	inland lakes with gravel substrate (only known at four sites in UK)

Great crested newt

What do they look like?

Adult great crested newts can reach a total length of 110–170 mm. The common and palmate newt are approximately half the length of a great crested newt.

Great crested newts (*Triturus cristatus*) are black or dark brown with darker spots. During the breeding season males have a jagged crest along the back with a white or silver stripe on the tail.

Juveniles resemble adult females but are smaller and may be confused with adult common or palmate newts.

Natural history

Great crested newts (GCN) breed in ponds but spend the majority of their time on land, foraging and sheltering. Therefore they should be considered when working on land as well as ponds.

Habitat requirements

PENALTIES

Offences are punishable by fines of up to £5000 per offence (for example, disturbance with an excavator to a pond containing GCN). Penalties may also include prison sentences of up to six months. In addition, any vehicle used to commit the offence may be forfeited. Either the company and/or individuals may be held liable. Penalties may be higher where dealt with in crown court.

- across lowland areas in England, Wales and Scotland (not Northern Ireland) in a range of habitats including farmland, semi-natural grassland, woodland, mineral extraction sites, urban and suburban sites (such as parks and gardens), dewponds and sand-dune pools.

- can be found in ponds 50 to 300 m^2 in size, and have been known to breed in a range of wetlands – including temporary balancing or drainage pools

- the majority of adult newts return to the same breeding pond year after year

- when on land, will normally remain within 250–500 m of the breeding pond, although on occasions they may move over 1 km

- prefer mixed vegetation, including rough tussocky grassland, scrub, woodland and hedgerow and also use underground crevices, mammal burrows and rock piles.

Legal protection

Without a development licence, it is illegal to kill, injure or disturb GCN or to damage, destroy or obstruct places they use for shelter or protection.

The GCN has a bright yellow/orange underside with dark spots

- the EA or SEPA must be consulted wherever works may impact on wetlands and watercourses. Consent may be required

- Great crested newts and their habitat are fully protected under the Wildlife and Countryside Act 1981 (as amended), and the Habitats Regulations 1994.

It is illegal to:

- intentionally or deliberately capture, kill or injure great crested newts

- intentionally, deliberately or recklessly* damage, destroy or obstruct access to any place used for shelter or protection, including resting or breeding places (occupied or not)

- deliberately, intentionally or recklessly* disturb great crested newts when in a place of shelter

- sell, barter, exchange or transport or offer for sale great crested newts or parts of them.

The legislation covers all life stages: eggs, larvae, juveniles and adults.

*   For England and Wales the term "reckless" was added as an amendment to the *Wildlife and Countryside Act 1981*, as a result of the *CRoW Act 2000*.

Other legislation and nature conservation guidance

Newts that have been captured are also protected by UK animal welfare legislation, which prohibits cruelty. The Great crested newts is listed as a priority species under the *UK Biodiversity Action Plan*.

Licensing for development

Before undertaking any development or mitigation works that will affect great crested newts or certain parts of their habitat, a development licence must first be obtained from Defra, SEERAD or the WA. This will be granted only to a suitably-experienced person and will depend on evidence of adequate surveys and mitigation plans. Licences take 30 days or more to be granted.

Surveys

Wherever development will affect ponds – or land within 500 m of an existing GCN pond, SNCOs recommend that surveys should be conducted to inform an assessment of impacts and possible mitigation measures.

A suitable GCN habitat

Pond surveys are conducted over several weeks. Surveys of the land within 500 m of a great crested newt pond will require at least 2–3 months. See table on pages 34–36 for timing of surveys.

WHAT IF GCN ARE FOUND ON SITE AFTER WORKS HAVE STARTED?

If GCN are found on site after works have started, **works in the area must stop immediately**. Consult an expert for advice on how to proceed. Works may need to be delayed until mitigation can be conducted at the appropriate time of year.

Mitigation

Where impacts are completely unavoidable, mitigation measures will need to be agreed and set in place before works go ahead.

Mitigation works may take many weeks or months to complete and in some cases can run into the following year. Any mitigation measures will normally need to be put in place **before the actual development work can proceed**.

The timing of mitigation must take other protected species on site into consideration – for example, clearance of vegetation may affect bats, reptiles and nesting birds.

- *Compensation for loss of great crested newts habitat* – any loss of GCN habitat, including both ponds and terrestrial habitat, must be compensated for through habitat creation. This may include the creation of new ponds, sheltering sites (hibernacula) and planting to provide dense ground cover.

- *New ponds* should be created at least one year before their intended use by GCN. For every pond lost, two new ones should be created.

Why do they need special protection?
- they have shown a rapid decline across many parts of Europe over the last century.

- reasons for this decline include the destruction or neglect of pond habitats, land fragmentation through agriculture and urbanisation, land drainage, fish introductions and pollution.

- *Translocation of GCN* – where a pond or an area of land where great crested newts occur is to be lost, it may be necessary to move animals into a suitable safe area. However, this should be considered only as a last resort and only under a development licence.

Capture of all newts from an area can take upwards of *30 days* and the trapping period may extend to as much as *three years*.

Positive impacts through development

- creation of ponds or groups of ponds

- leaving small piles of wood and rocks as feeding, hibernation and sheltering sites

- creation of new areas of terrestrial habitat and hibernacula using spoil and debris from construction works

- use of sustainable drainage systems (SUDS) wherever possible and avoiding use of gulleypots.

Carrying out appropriate surveys at the right time can prevent long and costly delays that could occur if newts are found once works begin.

What else might I see?

Great crested newts commonly occur alongside the smooth newt, palmate newt, common frog and common toad. These species are all protected against sale, and against cruelty. Disturbance of these species does not require a licence.

The smooth and palmate newt are approximately half the length of GCN and their back is brown rather than black.

Alien species

A number of amphibians and reptiles have been introduced into the UK. These include the European pond terrapin and red-eared terrapin, bull frog, marsh frog and alpine newt.

European pond terrapin

In some cases, such as the bull frog and red-eared terrapin, introduced species cause damage to British wildlife and are considered pests.

If you capture any alien species, put them in a cool damp container and consult an expert. Do not re-release them into the wild.

THE GREAT CRESTED NEWT YEAR

	Key
	Peak numbers
	Moderate numbers
	Few individuals

Behaviour	J	F	M	A	M	J	J	A	S	O	N	D
Adults hibernation or low activity on land												
Adults active and feeding on land												
Adults in breeding pond												
Egg-laying												
Larvae present in ponds												
Larvae changing into juveniles and leaving ponds												
Juveniles on land												

Invertebrates

WHAT DO WE NEED TO KNOW ABOUT INVERTEBRATES?

There are almost 30 000 species of invertebrate in the UK, excluding microscopic species.

Common blue butterfly

Of those that have been identified so far, there are approximately 6000 species of flies, 6500 bees and wasps, 4000 beetles, 2500 butterflies and moths, 1800 bugs, 1600 other insect species, 3000 spiders and mites, and 3600 other invertebrate species (crustaceans, annelids, molluscs etc).

The most familiar species are those that are regularly seen, such as slugs, snails, spiders, flies, butterflies and beetles.

Natural history

There are great variations in the natural history of different invertebrate species. Some species are solitary while others live in large social groups. Well-known examples of the latter are ants and some species of wasp and bee.

The length of their life cycle varies too. For example, stag beetle larvae live up to seven years, while the adult stag beetle generally lives only a few months. In other species, eg some butterfly and moth species, the adult phase lasts only a few hours. Many invertebrate species are inactive during winter.

Habitat requirements

Invertebrates are likely to occur on every development site. They live in the soil, among ground vegetation, in trees and shrubs, in freshwater and marine water, in areas of bare ground and from the lowlands to the uplands. Even heavily polluted areas support a number of pollution-tolerant invertebrate species.

Legal protection

The *Wildlife and Countryside Act (WCA) 1981 (as amended)* and the *Wildlife Order 1985 (as amended)* currently lists 25 species of protected butterfly, eight species of moth, eight species of beetle, one species hemipteran bug, three species of cricket, two species of dragonfly, two species of spider, four species of crustacean (eg white-clawed crayfish), one species of sea-mat, nine species of mollusc (eg sandbowl snail). three species of annelid worm and four species of sea anemone.

The table on the facing page shows how the level of protection varies from those that receive full protection to those that are protected against killing and injury, damage and/or destruction of their place of shelter, or taking. Some species are protected against sale only.

For those species receiving *full protection*, it is an offence to:

■ intentionally kill, injure or capture

■ intentionally or recklessly* disturb

■ intentionally or recklessly* damage, destroy or obstruct places of shelter or protection, including breeding sites (occupied or not)

■ possess or transport an animal (or any part thereof) unless under licence

■ sell or exchange animals.

* In England and Wales, the term "reckless" has been added as an amendment to the *WCA 1981* as result of the *CRoW Act 2000*, and in Scotland as a result of the *Nature Conservation (Scotland) Act 2004.*

All of the legislation covers all life stages, ie eggs, larvae, juveniles and adults. The habitats used during the egg and larval stages are often completely different from those used during the adult life stage.

In addition to protection afforded through the **Wildlife and Countryside Act 1981**, the large blue (*Maculinea arion*), an extremely rare butterfly, receives full protection in England, Wales and Scotland under the **Habitats Regulations 1994.**

Key to level of protection (facing page):
Fully protected at all times
Protected against killing, injury, possession and sale
Protected against killing, injury, possession, sale and taking
Protected against damage, destruction or obstruction of a place used for shelter or protection
Protected against taking and sale
Protected against sale only

Protected in England, Wales & Scotland (*WCA*)			Northern Ireland (*WO*)
Butterflies	Fisher's estuarine	Crustaceans	
Large blue	Barberry carpet	White-clawed crayfish*	Butterflies
Heath fritillary	Black-veined	Fairy shrimp	Brimstone
Swallowtail	Sussex emerald	Lagoon sand shrimp	Dingy skipper
High brown fritillary	Essex emerald	Apus	Holly blue
Marsh fritillary	New Forest burnet	Sea-mats	Large heath
Large copper	Beetles	Trembling sea-mat	Marsh fritillary
Purple emperor	Rainbow leaf beetle	Molluscs	Purple hairstreak
Northern brown argus	Mire pill beetle	Fan mussel	Small blue
Pearl bordered fritillary	*Graphoderus zonatus* (water beetle)	De Folin's lagoon snail	Molluscs
Checkered skipper	Lesser silver water beetle	Sandbowl snail	Freshwater mussel
Large heath	*Hypebaeus flavipes* (beetle)	Pearl mussel	Common sea-urchin
Small blue	Violet click beetle	Glutinous snail	
Mountain ringlet	Stag beetle	*Paludinella littorina*	
Duke of burgundy	*Paracymus aeneus* (water beetle)	(Lagoon snail)	
Silver-spotted skipper	Hemipteran bugs	Lagoon sea slug	
Wood white	New Forest cicada	Northern hatchet-shell	
Adonis blue	Crickets	Annelid worms	
Chalkhill blue	Wart-biter	Tentacled lagoon worm	
Glanville fritillary	Mole cricket	Lagoon sandworm	
Large tortoiseshell	Field cricket	Medicinal leech	
Silver-studded blue	Dragonflies	Sea anemones and allies	
Black hairstreak	Norfolk aeshna	Marine hydroid	
White-letter hairstreak	Southern damselfly	Ivell's sea anemone	
Brown hairstreak	Spiders	Pink sea-fan	
Lulworth skipper	Fen raft spider	Starlet sea-anemone	
Moths	Ladybird spider		
Reddish buff			
Fiery clearwing			

* White-clawed (Atlantic stream) crayfish is currently proposed for addition to Schedule 5 of the *Wildlife Order (NI) 1985*.

Other legislation and nature conservation guidance

Many species of invertebrates that are *not* listed under the legislation are of conservation concern and are listed under the *UK Biodiversity Action Plan*. A large number of invertebrates are listed as priority BAP species for which action plans have been developed (more than 250 species – the full list can be obtained from the UK Biodiversity Action Plan website). However, many of these are rare and are unlikely to occur on the vast majority of sites affected by construction projects.

For certain species, such as the stag beetle, guidelines have been issued by EN, SNH, CCW, EHS and/or the wildlife trusts, to mitigate against the impact of development on these species.

Licensing for development

There is no provision for SNCOs to issue licences permitting development. However, to avoid prosecution, it must be shown that all reasonable effort was made to avoid breaking the law. This requires adequate surveys and mitigation plans before undertaking any works that will impact on protected invertebrate species (including mitigation works). It is therefore essential to seek advice from an experienced ecologist, who should liaise with EN, SNH, EHS-NH (NI) or CCW.

In England, Scotland and Wales, before conducting any development or mitigation works that will affect the large blue butterfly or its habitat, a development licence must first be obtained from Defra, the WA or SEERAD. This will be granted only to a suitably-qualified ecologist and will depend on evidence of adequate surveys and mitigation plans. In practice the large blue is so rare, and its habitats protected, that this is unlikely to arise.

Surveys and mitigation

Where necessary, evidence of adequate surveys and mitigation will be required to prove that every reasonable effort will be or was made to avoid killing or injuring protected invertebrates.

Surveys can be undertaken only at certain times of the year, which vary depending on the species in question. Surveys will also need to be conducted at an appropriated time of day and in suitable weather, again dependent on the species concerned.

Where survey methods involve capture or disturbance of species that are protected under the **WCA 1981**, a personal surveying licence must be obtained from the relevant SNCO.

Survey methods

Surveys for adults can be conducted only at specific times of year. In certain species, the adult phase lasts only for a matter of hours or days. Surveys at other times of year will need to focus on pre-adult life stages, ie eggs, larvae and juveniles.

The survey method used depends on:

- the life cycle of the species concerned
- the time of year at which surveys are conducted
- whether surveys are focused on the adult or pre-adults life stages.

Survey methods include:

- walkover surveys inspecting living and decaying vegetation, including tree stumps, logs etc
- pitfall trapping
- netting
- use of light-traps or similar
- vacuum sampling.

Surveys may be conducted during the day or night depending on the behaviour patterns of the species concerned.

WHAT IF PROTECTED SPECIES ARE FOUND ON SITE AFTER WORKS HAVE STARTED?

If protected species of invertebrate are found on site after works have started, **works in the area must stop immediately**, as it is illegal to disturb fully protected species, or to damage or obstruct their habitat. It is also illegal to kill or injure some species. If in doubt, consult an expert.

Works may need to be delayed until mitigation can be conducted at the appropriate time of year.

Mitigation for invertebrates

If impacts on protected invertebrate species cannot be avoided, mitigation measures will be required. The type and scale of mitigation will depend on the type and scale of the impact.

Banded demoiselle damselfly

The following guidance is for general information only. Mitigation must always be designed and conducted on a case-by-case basis and in consultation with an expert. All mitigation proposals should be agreed with the relevant SNCO.

Depending on the site, mitigation measures may include:

- maintaining continuity of important habitat features, such as patches of sunny bare ground, vertical banks, dead trees and ruderal plants

- maintaining structural diversity of vegetation: for grassland this can be done by avoiding frequent cutting and keeping some areas of bare ground

- avoiding over-planting of sites: eg not planting trees in a previously open site, as this could result in the loss of vulnerable species

- creating mosaics of scrub and grassland land using native species of local provenance

- allowing natural colonisation by ruderal plants, rather than importing topsoil and using seed or grass mixes

- retaining dead wood on site, including logs, stumps and windblown trees

- leaving dead trees standing (provided they do not represent a health or safety hazard);

- ensuring that suitable invertebrate habitat is linked via appropriate wildlife corridors or flight lines

- safeguarding waterways against pollution.

Translocation of habitat has low success rates, is expensive and should be used only as a last resort.

Positive impacts through development

As part of development and landscaping, areas can be enhanced for invertebrates by:

- building "loggeries" from natural wood at woodland edges and in shady areas which will benefit many invertebrate species, including stag beetles

- constructing artificial breeding boxes for stag beetles from hardwood timber

- laying a number of flat stones around the site to provide shelter for species such as centipedes and ground beetles

- creating "mosaic" habitats, eg a combination of areas of scrub, grassland and woodland

Green bush cricket

- creating a pond with shallow margins and lots of semi-aquatic plants, to attract breeding insects such as dragonflies

- providing nesting areas for solitary wasps and bees (eg tins filled with bamboo canes and drilled blocks of wood)

- creating sparsely vegetated steep slopes/shallow vertical cliffs, to provide micro-habitats for burrowing bees, wasps and other species.

INVERTEBRATES ON CONSTRUCTION SITES

Occasionally some species of invertebrate can cause problems on construction sites. Such species may include:

- **masonry or mortar bees** – which are capable of damaging buildings by burrowing. This kind of activity takes place in early spring and summer and noticeable damage is likely to occur if large numbers become established in a small area. The most effective method of dealing with this problem is to repoint the walls in which mortar joints are being attacked. This should be done when the bees are active and absent from the nest, to allow them to find alternative nest sites

- **wasps** – which can be a nuisance when nests are close to human activity. If wasp nests are to be treated, the best time of year to do this is June. Wasps survive for just one year and die when temperatures fall to freezing, therefore if it is late in the season wasp nests can be left alone.

Any insecticides used should be those approved under the **Pesticides Safety Precautions Scheme.** *Pest control measures may be illegal if they impact on protected species. It is strongly recommended that a registered pest control company is used.*

Protected plants

WHAT DO WE NEED TO KNOW ABOUT PROTECTED PLANTS?

Plants comprise trees, shrubs, herbs, ferns, grasses, mosses, liverworts, algae and lichens. Fungi are also sometimes classified as plants but are now generally considered to belong to their own special category.

The identification of plants to species level is a skilled job, and only an experienced botanist or ecologist should be employed to identify protected or rare plant species in relation to a potential development project.

Legal protection

Plants are protected by law. The *Wildlife and Countryside Act 1981 (as amended)* and the *Wildlife (NI) Order 1985* make it an offence for any person who is not "authorised" to intentionally uproot any wild plant. An "authorised" person can be the owner or occupier of the land on which the action is taken, or anybody authorised by them; or any person authorised in writing by the local authority for the area within which the action is taken.

> **PENALTIES**
>
> **Offences are punishable by fines of up to £5000 per offence (for example, disturbance with an excavator to a pond containing GCN). Penalties may also include prison sentences of up to six months. In addition, any vehicle used to commit the offence may be forfeited. Either the company and/or individuals may be held liable. Penalties may be higher where dealt with in crown court.**

In addition, the *Wildlife and Countryside Act 1981 (as amended)* and the *Wildlife Order 1985* also includes, within *Schedule 8*, in the order of 60 plant species that it is illegal for *any person* to intentionally pick, uproot or destroy.

> If fully-protected species are found on site **work must stop** and appropriate mitigation discussed with the SNCO.

The *Habitats Regulations 1994* include a list within *Schedule 4* of nine species of European protected plants whose natural range includes Great Britain. The regulations make it an offence, among other things, to deliberately pick, collect, cut, uproot or destroy any of these plants.

To avoid breaking the law, the presence/absence of the species that are protected by legislation must be verified by an experienced botanist.

Other legislation and nature conservation guidance

Some plants are also listed within various international conventions including the **Berne Convention 1974** and **CITES**. However, the legal protection of these plants is provided by the Acts mentioned above.

Licensing for development

When a development affects plant species protected under the **Wildlife and Countryside Act 1981** or the **Wildlife (NI) Order 1985**, there is generally no provision for granting licences. Works that contravene the law will rely on the defence that all reasonable effort was made to avoid breaking the law – this requires evidence of adequate surveys and mitigation. It is therefore essential to seek advice from an experienced ecologist.

Bee orchid

PRACTICAL MEASURES FOR DEALING WITH PLANTS ON SITE

While the very rare species of plants are fully protected by the law, a large number of uncommon species receive scant protection. Where the latter are found on development sites, while it is not illegal to destroy them, steps should be taken to avoid their loss whenever possible.

Mitigation may include

- fencing off areas where rare or protected plants occur

- erection of warning signs

- avoiding pollution by dust or run-off

- preventing spread of invasive species

- habitat translocation (see box right)

- collecting seed or other propagules and re-introducing the species post-development or utilising them in off-site mitigation

- planting of species which are appropriate to the site.

Translocation of plants

Where avoidance of impacts is impossible and the species or habitat are considered rare or sufficiently unusual, translocation should be considered. Rarer plants tend to be very particular in respect of environmental conditions, including the other species of plant among which they are able to grow. It is important to ensure that, in dealing with these rare plants, conditions are maintained or recreated similar to those in which the species or habitat was originally found.

Positive impacts through development

Wherever possible plan for and design in new wild areas using plants typically found in the vicinity of the place that you are developing. Consult the local BAP and consider whether or not some of the plant species referred to within it can be introduced within your project. Large scale infrastructure projects rely on the "healing power of nature" to help blend them into the surrounding landscape. The opportunity for those and similar projects to contribute in a positive way to local BAPs is potentially very great.

Where to go for further help and guidance

Organisations that can be contacted for advice on protected plants:

- SNCOs

- Plantlife

- local wildlife trusts

- Botanical Society of the British Isles.

Bluebells under coppiced hazel

Reptiles

IDENTIFYING REPTILES

Common lizards (*Lacerta vivipara*) typically grow up to 135 mm long and are various shades of brown with small bars or spots.

Sand lizard

Sand lizards (*Lacerta agilis*) typically grow up to 165 mm long. They are brown, grey or sandy coloured with stripes and spots with white centres. Males have bright green sides.

Slow-worm

Slow-worms (*Anguis fragilis*) grow up to 400 mm long. They are really legless lizards, but have a snake-like appearance.

Adder

Adders (*Vipera berus*) can grow up to 550 mm long. They have a dark-coloured zig-zag stripe all the way along the upper part of their body.

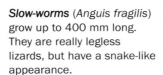

Grass snakes (*Natrix natrix*) grow up to 750 mm long. They are olive-green with small lines and spots and have a yellow or orange collar at the neck.

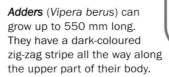

Smooth snakes (*Coronella austriaca*) grow up to 600 mm long. They are grey or brown with two rows of dark coloured spots and a black heart-shaped marking on the head.

Smooth snake

Species	England	Scotland	Wales	N. Ireland
Common lizard	■	■	■	■
Slow-worm	■	■	■	
Grass snake	■		■	
Adder	■	■	■	
Sand lizard	■		■	
Smooth snake	■			

Note: species have been recorded in these countries but may be found in new areas. Always consult an expert.

REPTILES – NATURAL HISTORY AND HABITAT PREFERENCES

- reptiles are active during the day in spring, summer and autumn, generally from March to early October

- they hibernate through the winter from October to March.

Habitat

- reptiles may be found in both rural and urban areas among vegetation or sheltering under logs, rocks and compost heaps, or basking in open sunlight

- suitable areas, preferably with some sunny hollows and south-facing banks, include heathland, scrub, rough grassland, moorland, railway embankments, churchyards and hedgerows

- common lizards and slow-worms are the most commonly found reptile species in Britain. The common lizard is the only native reptile found in Northern Ireland

- grass snakes are more frequently associated with water

- the smooth snake and sand lizard are both very rare. They occur in sandy heathland habitats in Surrey, Hampshire, Dorset and Sussex. The sand lizard also occurs on sand dune habitat in Merseyside and has been re-introduced to North Wales.

All native British reptiles are protected against intentional killing and injury under the *Wildlife and Countryside Act 1981 (as amended)* and the *Wildlife (NI) Order 1985*.

Furthermore the *sand lizard* and *smooth snake* are **fully protected** under the *Wildlife and Countryside Act 1981 (as amended)*, and the *Habitats Regulations 1994*, making it illegal to:

Why do they need special protection?

- all six species of British reptile have been identified as being of conservation concern, because of the decline in suitable habitat.

- deliberately or intentionally kill, capture or injure sand lizards or smooth snakes
- deliberately, intentionally or recklessly* disturb sand lizards or smooth snakes
- deliberately, intentionally or recklessly* damage, destroy or obstruct a breeding site, resting place or other place used for shelter and protection
- take or destroy eggs
- keep, sell, or exchange sand lizards or smooth snakes (or their eggs).

* For England and Wales the term "recklessly" was added in as an amendment to the *Wildlife and Countryside Act 1981* as a result of the *CRoW Act 2000,* and for Scotland the *Nature Conservation (Scotland) Act 2004.*

In England, Scotland and Wales, slow-worm, common lizard, adder and grass snake are also protected against killing, injury and sale, barter or exchange, but their habitats or places of shelter are not specifically protected.

In Northern Ireland the **common (or "viviparous") lizard** receives *full protection* at all times under Schedule 5 of the *Wildlife (NI) Order 1985*, making it illegal to:

- intentionally kill, capture or injure common lizards
- disturb a common lizard while it is occupying a structure or place which it uses for shelter or protection
- damage, destroy or obstruct any structure or place used for shelter or protection
- possess, sell or exchange common lizards.

All the above legislation applies to all life stages (eggs, juveniles and adults).

Other legislation and nature conservation guidance

All animals that have been captured are also protected by UK animal welfare legislation that prohibits cruelty and abandonment.

The sand lizard is a priority species under the *UK Biodiversity Action Plan* (BAP). Reptiles may also be included in local biodiversity action plans.

Licensing for development

In England, Scotland and Wales, a development licence must be obtained from Defra or the WA before undertaking any development works that will affect **sand lizards** and **smooth snakes** or their habitat. Licences will be granted only to suitably-experienced persons and will depend on evidence of adequate surveys and mitigation plans. Licences take 30 days or more to be granted.

In Northern Ireland, to avoid prosecution when development works will affect **common lizards** or their habitat, evidence is required that all reasonable effort was made to avoid breaking the law – proof of adequate surveys and mitigation will be needed. EHS-NH (NI) should be consulted to decide whether a conservation licence may be appropriate.

For development sites in *England, Wales or Scotland*, to avoid prosecution under the *Wildlife and Countryside Act 1981 (as amended)*, wherever works will impact on slow-worms, common lizards, adders and/or grass snakes there must be evidence that every reasonable effort was made to avoid breaking the law – including proof of adequate surveys and mitigation plans. Mitigation measures should, ideally, be agreed with the relevant SNCO.

Surveys

Wherever a proposed development includes areas of suitable habitat for any native species of reptile, surveys should be undertaken by a suitably-experienced person. (See table on pages 34–36. for timing).

Reptiles prefer a mosaic of different habitats, including grass, scrub and open areas

Mitigation

Where impacts are completely unavoidable, mitigation measures will need to be agreed and set in place *before works go ahead*. The timing of mitigation works may be restricted, for instance capture programmes can be undertaken only when reptiles are active (ie between March and September). Even within this period, weather conditions may restrict the timing of trapping programmes further.

What if reptiles are found on site after works have started?

If reptiles are found on site after development has started, **works must stop immediately.**

Works may need to be delayed until mitigation can be conducted at the appropriate time of year.

Translocation

1   Where loss of reptile habitat is completely unavoidable, and since all native reptile species are protected against killing and injury at the very least, reptile species occurring on a development site will need to be excluded through trapping and the use of reptile fencing, before any vegetation clearance can take place. Alternative habitats must be available to which the reptiles can move. Projects affecting sand lizards or smooth snakes will require a licence. Where small areas of habitat are to be lost, exclusion of reptiles by habitat management (eg strimming), may be acceptable. Check with the SNCO first.

2   Habitat creation is likely to be required eg construction of hibernaculum or log pile refugia and areas of grassland.

3   Guidance on the length of time required to capture all reptiles from an area ranges upwards of 60 "suitable" days; the capture period may extend to two years or more.

The timing of mitigation must take other protected species into consideration (for example, scrub clearance may also affect nesting birds and great crested newts).

Positive impacts through development

Habitats can be easily improved for reptiles as part of post-development landscaping as follows:

■ use of spoil to create south-facing banks for basking

■ creation of rock and log pile sheltering places using debris from clearance and construction

■ creation of mosaics of scrub and grassland.

Always obtain specialist advice on a case-by-case basis before carrying out any of these measures.

Reptile survey using a sheet of corrugated tin as an artificial refuge

What else might I see?

The **common wall lizard** and the **red-eared terrapin** are introduced species that have been released in various areas by private owners. If you capture these species do not let them go again – put them in a cool container with some shelter and consult an expert.

Reptile fencing can be used to keep reptiles out of a site

Log piles or piles of stones provide refugia for reptiles and amphibians

Where to go for further help and guidance

Organisations that can be contacted for expert advice on reptiles:

● Herpetofauna Conservation Trust
● Froglife
● local amphibian and reptile groups
● SNCOs

Useful references:

● Gent, T and Gibson, S (eds) *Herpetofauna Workers Manual* (JNCC, 2003)

THE REPTILE YEAR

	Key
■	Hibernation
	Low/moderate activity
	Mating, egg laying/pregnancy
	Hatching/birth of young

Month	J	F	M	A	M	J	J	A	S	O	N	D
Common lizard												
Slow-worm												
Grass snake												
Adder												
Sand lizard												
Smooth snake												

Otter

IDENTIFYING OTTERS

Otters (*Lutra lutra*) have long slender bodies, short legs, a flattened head with a broad muzzle, small eyes and ears, and a thick tapered tail. They are quite large animals, approximately 1 m long, and have dark brown fur on the back and a pale underside.

- otters swim low with only nose and eyes visible above the water

- they are active all year round and can breed at any time.

Habitat

Otters are found in both rural and urban areas in England, parts of Wales, Northern Ireland and Scotland.

They rest and breed in dens known as "holts" – including holes in river banks or hollow trees, cavities in rock or log piles and tree roots, flood debris, caves and man-made structures.

- cubs may be raised in holts or on couches up to 500 m away from water

- otters will use any size of watercourse and need plenty of vegetation cover

- otters are found on rivers, canals, lakes and reservoirs, occasionally estuaries and coasts, plus floodplain areas, including well-vegetated streams, ponds, bogs, marshes, dyke networks, fens, reedbeds, islands, and woodland.

Otter signs

Otters are mostly active at night and are nervous of humans, so sightings are rare. Signs include:

- "spraints" (droppings) – a mass of fish bones and scales held together by a sticky green-black substance, left in prominent places such as on heaps of earth or grass, along runs and on ledges, boulders, overhanging branches etc
- dens and flattened areas within dense vegetation
- footprints – webbed with five toes, approximately 50 mm across
- worn paths alongside watercourses.

Legal protection

Without a development licence, it is an offence to kill, injure or disturb otters or to damage, destroy or obstruct places used for shelter or protection.

Details of the legislation are as follows:

Otters and their habitat are fully protected under the *Wildlife and Countryside Act 1981 (as amended)*, the *Wildlife Order (NI) 1985* and the *Habitats Regulations 1994* and *(NI) 1995.*

It is an offence to:

- intentionally or deliberately kill, injure or capture otters
- intentionally or recklessly* disturb otters
- intentionally or recklessly* damage, destroy or obstruct breeding or resting sites or places used for shelter or protection (holts, couches etc) – whether occupied or not
- possess or transport an otter (or any part thereof) unless under licence
- sell or exchange otters.

*   In England and Wales the term "reckless" has been added as an amendment to the *Wildlife and Countryside Act 1981* as a result of the *CRoW Act 2000,* and in Scotland the *Nature Conservation (Scotland) Act 2004.*

Other legislation and nature conservation guidance

Otters are also protected under the *Wild Mammals (Protection) Act 1996* and the *Welfare of Animals Act 1972*, which protects animals against cruelty.

The otter and many of its habitats are listed as priorities under the *UK Biodiversity Action Plan (BAP)*.

Surveys

Otters may be expected on any watercourse. Wherever developments are proposed in habitat that is potentially suitable for otters, including minor works such as improvements or maintenance works to small bridges or culverts, surveys must be conducted by a suitably-experienced specialist.

Where surveys show that otters are present, *all* efforts must be made to avoid *any* impacts on the animals.

Surveys may need to be repeated during the run-up to works and immediately before works start, particularly in cases where there is a long lead-in time to a development.

Surveys must be undertaken only by people who are suitably trained and experienced in recognising otter signs. Where survey methods are invasive, a survey licence must be obtained from EN, CCW, EHS-N(NI) or SNH.

Licensing for development

Before undertaking any development or mitigation works that will impact on otters or any structures or places they use for shelter or protection, a development licence must first be obtained from Defra, SEERAD, EHS-NH (NI) or the WA. These will be granted only to a suitably-qualified person and will depend on evidence of adequate surveys and mitigation plans. Licences can take 30 days or more to be granted.

Why do otters need special protection?

- a dramatic decline since the 1950s left only a few, isolated otter populations

- extensive conservation efforts have enabled the otter to re-occupy much of its former range

- the UK otter population is of European and international importance.

Survey methods

Generally, surveys can be undertaken at any time of year, as otters are active all year round and can breed at any time. In some parts of the UK, however, there is evidence of seasonality.

Otters are shy creatures and like to have plenty of vegetation cover to hide in

Initial surveys of small areas can sometimes be completed within one day or less, but may take considerably longer, depending on the size and complexity of the site. Furthermore, if otters are suspected of breeding on the site, intensive, longer-term surveys may be required.

Repeat surveys may be required depending on the outcome of initial surveys, the scale of the impact and the nature of the proposed works. For example, repeat surveys may not be required if works are of a sufficiently small scale and they would not involve any possible destruction or disturbance of potential holt or den sites. However, the need for surveys must always be assessed on a case-by-case basis, in consultation with a suitably experienced person and agreed with the relevant SNCO and consenting bodies.

What if otters are found on site after works have started?
If otters are found on site after works have started **works in the area must stop immediately.**

The first step must be for an experienced surveyor to undertake a survey to establish the extent to which otters are using the site (ie whether they are resident, breeding or passing through).

Depending on survey results, works may need to be delayed until mitigation can be conducted at the appropriate time of year.

 **Otters are often confused with mink (a non-protected species in the UK), although mink are much smaller.**

Mitigation for otters

The following provides general information on possible mitigation measures.

Mitigation

Where impacts are completely unavoidable, mitigation measures will need to be agreed and set in place *before works go ahead*. A mitigation plan will need to be included in Development Licence applications. The timing of mitigation works may be restricted, for instance if otters are breeding on site.

The EA, SEPA or EHS-EP(NI) must be consulted wherever works affect watercourses or wetlands. Consents may be required.

Destruction of holts or couches should be avoided at all costs.

Exclusion fencing can be used to prevent disturbance of areas used by otters. However, if otters are breeding on a site this may not be sufficient and it may be necessary to delay works until otters are no longer dependent on the natal holt. This will reduce the risk of young being abandoned due to disturbance.

- safe working distances must be agreed with the relevant SNCO
- any pollution of watercourses from run-off, building waste or rubbish must be avoided
- the treatment of banks, viaducts etc may be subject to consent from EA, SEPA or EHS-EP (NI). The Highways Agency's Design Manual for Roads and Bridges provides specific guidance concerning otters.

General mitigation measures may also include:

- provision of safe river and road crossing points
- otter-proof fencing along roads
- construction of artificial holts
- maintenance of habitat corridors
- use of ledges and underpasses beneath bridges, through culverts etc
- mitigation for the effects of a scheme on otter food sources, such as fish and amphibians.

Mitigation works may take many weeks or months to complete and in some cases can run into the following year. Any mitigation measures will normally need to be put in place *before the development work can proceed.* Avoiding impacts in the first place is always the better option.

The timing of mitigation must take other protected species on site into consideration – such as water voles and fish.

Positive impacts through development

- providing simple structures for otters to shelter in or under, such as rock piles, felled trees etc

- construction of artificial log-pile or chamber holts

- creation of otter havens through planting of bank-side and uncultivated buffer zones

- creation of "soft" banks, using gabions and boulders, rather than concrete, to provide hard protection where required

- using bridges instead of culverts or, where culverts must be used, using box culverts

- use of viaducts or wide-span bridges.

Where to go for further help and guidance

Organisations that can be contacted for expert advice on otters:

- The Environment Agency
- wildlife trusts

Useful references:

- Design Manual for Roads and Bridges (Highways Agency 2001)
- Nature Conservation on Roads: advice in relation to otters (Highways Agency / Wildlife Conservation Research Unit).

Pine marten

WHAT DO THEY LOOK LIKE?

Pine martens (*Martes martes*) have a slender, cat-sized body with long legs, dark brown fur with a yellow or white throat patch and a long bushy tail.

They are smaller than otters and badgers, but larger than stoats, weasels, polecats and mink.

Pine martens are nocturnal, hunting through the night and especially at dusk. They are very agile, climbing trees in a similar manner to squirrels.

Natural history

Pine martens are solitary animals. They maintain territories of between four and 15 km^2.

Though mainly nocturnal they are active during the day in summer.

Pine martens mate in July or August and have one litter per year comprising usually two or three young, which are born in spring (March to May).

The young may be seen outside in mid-June. They remain dependent on the female for three to six months.

Habitat requirements

Pine martens are now restricted mainly to Scotland and are rare in Northern Ireland. They are on the verge of extinction in northern England and north Wales, where only isolated populations remain. They are found in a wide range of habitats including native and non-native woodland, plantations and very open mountainous terrain.

Why do they need special protection?

- **Pine martens were once widespread, but persecution for their fur and by gamekeepers, as well as habitat fragmentation, has drastically reduced their range.**

They usually live at low densities, though this also depends on the quality of habitat. Pine martens may travel up to 28 km while hunting.

Pine marten den sites are difficult to find, but can occur in a variety of situations including hollow trees, rabbit burrows, rock holes, among the roots of fallen trees, in cairns and on scrub-covered cliffs. They also use old bird nests, bird nest boxes and are occasionally found in buildings.

Pine martens tend to use several dens scattered throughout their territory.

Legal protection

Pine martens are fully protected under the *Wildlife and Countryside Act (1981)* and the *Wildlife Order (NI) 1985*. It is an offence to:

- intentionally kill, injure or capture pine martens
- intentionally or recklessly* disturb pine martens while they are occupying a structure or place of shelter or protection
- intentionally or recklessly* damage, destroy or obstruct breeding sites or other places of shelter
- possess or transport a pine marten (or any part thereof) unless under licence
- sell or exchange pine martens.

The legislation covers all life stages – juveniles and adults.

* In England and Wales the term "reckless" was added as an amendment to the *Wildlife and Countryside Act 1981* as a result of the *CRoW Act 2000*, and in Scotland by the *Nature Conservation (Scotland) Act 2004.*

Pine marten signs

When surveying it is more common to see signs of pine martens, rather than the animals themselves.

- pine marten droppings are are 50–80 mm long, similar to those of foxes, tapered and very twisted
- droppings can be found every 100 to 200 m along territory boundaries such as forest roads and paths, on mounds of soil, trees and large boulders etc
- close to dens, droppings are deposited as cone-shaped piles or latrines.

Other legislation and nature conservation guidance

Pine martens are also protected under the *Wild Mammals (Protection) Act 1996* and the *Welfare of Animals Act (NI)*, which protects all wild mammals against cruelty.

The pine marten is a species of conservation concern and is listed under the *UK Biodiversity Action Plan (BAP)*.

Licensing for development

There is currently no provision for SNCOs to issue licences to permit development or maintenance works affecting pine martens. In order to avoid prosecution, it must be shown that all reasonable effort was made to avoid breaking the law. This requires evidence of adequate surveys and mitigation.

The relevant SNCO should be contacted for guidance whenever works are expected to impact on pine martens.

Surveys and mitigation

Wherever development will impact on habitat that may be used by pine martens, surveys must be conducted by a suitably-experienced person.

Surveys for pine martens will need to be extremely thorough. It is very difficult to find either pine martens, their droppings or other field signs and their presence can easily go unnoticed. Absence should not be assumed on the basis of evidence being difficult to find.

The best time to conduct surveys for pine martens is in spring and summer, with at least some surveys undertaken *between March and May* to identify breeding dens. To allow for variation in activity and the fact that pine martens might be extending their range into new areas, surveys need to be repeated at various times throughout the year.

Surveys should not be conducted immediately after heavy rain or flooding when many signs may have been washed away.

Depending on the survey methods used, a personal SNCO "survey and monitoring" licence may be required.

Survey methods

Initial surveys involve a walk-over survey to identify field signs such as dens, droppings and footprints. If these suggest that pine martens are present, repeat surveys may be conducted using more intensive methods to estimate population density.

Each survey period will take a minimum of several days, depending on the area to be covered, and should be repeated immediately before works start.

WHAT IF PINE MARTENS ARE FOUND ON SITE AFTER WORKS HAVE STARTED?

If a pine marten or its shelter is found (or suspected) on site after works have started, *works in the area must stop immediately*, as it is an offence to injure, kill, capture or disturb pine martens, or to damage or obstruct any place or structure they use for shelter or protection. Consult an expert for advice on how to proceed.

Works may need to be delayed until mitigation can be conducted at the appropriate time of year.

Mitigation for pine martens

If impacts on pine martens or their habitat cannot be avoided, mitigation measures will be required. Mitigation will depend on the type and scale of the impact.

The following guidance is for general information only. Mitigation must always be designed and conducted on a case-by-case basis and in consultation with an expert.

All works and mitigation proposals must be agreed with the relevant SNCO.

Vegetation clearance and tree felling works should be conducted only outside of the breeding season, from *November to February,* and once mitigation measures have been agreed. Before starting any work, the area should be checked by an experienced specialist who should also be present while clearance work is being carried out.

Destruction of dens should be avoided at all costs and will require agreement from the relevant SNCO. Given the conservation status of pine martens it is unlikely that permission will be given to destroy a breeding den.

Mitigation measures should be implemented in advance of works or at the earliest possible stage in construction. They may include:

- protection of existing dens

- provision of safe road crossing points

- construction of artificial dens

- provision of nest boxes

- maintenance of habitat corridors

- planting of new woodland and scrub habitat

- post-construction monitoring.

Positive impact through development

Additional measures that can be incorporated to improve habitats for pine martens, include:

- planting and management of trees and vegetation cover to provide potential den sites and to increase populations of important food sources

- provision of nest boxes.

Always obtain specialist advice on a case-by-case basis before carrying out any of these measures.

Where to go for further help and guidance

Organisations that can be contacted for expert advice on pine martens:

- SNCOs

- The Vincent Wildlife Trust

- The Mammal Society

- Scottish Wildlife Trust

Red squirrel

WHAT DO THEY LOOK LIKE?

Red squirrels (*Sciurus vulgaris*) are between 180 and 240 mm big with a long and bushy tail.

Red squirrels can be distinguished from grey squirrels (*Sciurus carolinensis*) by their bright ginger to red or dark brown fur, only slightly tinged with grey in winter, and their much bushier ginger or red tail. They also have longer ear tufts than grey squirrels, especially in winter. Their tail and ear tufts sometimes gets a lighter tinge in summer.

Red squirrel

Natural history

Red squirrels are active during the day, but live at low densities and are now quite rare in Britain, so sightings are unusual.

Grey squirrels are an introduced species and are now more widespread than the red squirrel

They do not hibernate, but remain in their nest or drey during harsh weather. When active, they spend most of their time above ground in trees and shrubs.

Why do they need special protection?

- the red squirrel is Britain's only native squirrel. It has declined to extinction in many areas over the last 50 years following habitat loss and the introduction of the grey squirrel from North America

- it is now considered vulnerable in Britain.

Breeding can occur from December through to July. Litters of "kittens" are produced between March and May and/or July and September. Females have one or two litters per year. The most common number of young per litter is 2–3, but up to six can be produced.

Young red squirrels become independent after 10 to 12 weeks, when they may disperse up to 1.5 km. Red squirrels live for up to five years.

CIRIA C567

Habitat requirements

The red squirrel is now largely confined to northern England, Scotland and Ireland, with a few isolated populations in Wales and central and southern England.

Their preferred habitat consists of large blocks of a broad range of woodland types, including broadleaf. Throughout the UK they are now more often found in coniferous forests as a result of competition from grey squirrels which cannot adapt as well to coniferous forest as red squirrels. In the north of Scotland, where fewer grey squirrels occur, red squirrels are found in a much wider range of woodland habitats.

Squirrels feed on nuts, seeds, flowers, shoots and fungi. Their main food plants in deciduous woodland are hazel and hawthorn.

Red squirrels are dependent on continuous tree cover. In good habitat they can live at densities of one squirrel per hectare of woodland, but often the density is much lower. One red squirrel's territory can range from two to 10 ha.

Squirrel signs

Red squirrels are very rare and much more shy than grey squirrels. Rather than seeing the animals themselves it is more likely to find signs of red squirrels, which include nests, droppings and nutshells.

- nests or "dreys" are spherical and constructed from twigs and lined with soft hair, moss and dried grass

- dreys are usually located more than 6 m above ground next to the main trunk in tree forks, hollow trunks or branches, near the stem at the base of conifersas well as in bushes). Several squirrels may share the same drey.

Legal protection

Red squirrels and their habitat are fully protected under the *Wildlife and Countryside Act 1981* and the *Wildlife Order (NI) 1985*. It is an offence to:

- intentionally kill, injure or capture red squirrels

- intentionally or recklessly* disturb red squirrels while they are occupying a structure or place used for shelter or protection

- intentionally or recklessly* damage, destroy or obstruct breeding sites or other places of shelter and protection (nests, trees and bushes etc)

- possess or transport a red squirrel (or any part thereof), unless under licence

- sell or exchange red squirrels.

* In England and Wales the term "reckless" was as an amendment to the *Wildlife and Countryside Act 1981* as a result of the *CRoW Act 2000*, and in Scotland as a result of *the Nature Conservation (Scotland) Act 2004.*

The legislation covers all life stages, both juveniles and adults.

Other legislation and nature conservation guidance

Red squirrels are also protected under the *Wild Mammals (Protection) Act 1996*, which protects all wild mammals against cruelty and the *Welfare of Animals Act (NI) 1972*.

The red squirrel is listed as a priority species under the *UK Biodiversity Action Plan*.

Keeping within the law

To enable appropriate time-tabling of development works on sites where red squirrels may be present, the following three points should be considered.

1 Surveys are best undertaken during spring and summer. At least some surveys should be undertaken between March and May and/or July to September to enable breeding dens to be identified.

2 Where red squirrels are shown to be present, SNCOs require that impacts are avoided where at all possible, either through the use of alternative sites or redesign of the works. Where impacts are completely unavoidable, mitigation measures will need to be agreed and set in place before works go ahead. The timing of mitigation works may be restricted, for example, clearance in areas where red squirrels occur should be timed so as to avoid breeding periods and thus should be conducted only between August and November.

3 To avoid prosecution under the Wildlife and Countryside Act 1981 (as amended) or the Wildlife Order (NI) 1985, wherever works will impact on red squirrels there must be evidence that every reasonable effort was made to avoid breaking the law – including proof of adequate surveys and mitigation plans. Mitigation measures should be agreed with the relevant SNCO.

Licensing for development

Although there is no provision for SNCOs to issue development licences for works that will affect red squirrels or their habitat, to avoid prosecution, it must be shown that all reasonable effort was made to avoid breaking the law. This includes proof of adequate surveys and mitigation. The relevant SNCO should be contacted for guidance whenever works are expected to impact on red squirrels.

Where trees containing dreys have become unsafe and need to be felled, a licence can be issued by Defra, SEERAD, the WA or EHS-NH (NI) for reasons of public health and safety.

Surveys and mitigation

Wherever development will impact on habitat that may be used by red squirrels, surveys must be conducted by a suitably-experienced person.

All types of woodland are potentially suitable habitat for red squirrels. Where numbers of grey squirrels are lower, red squirrels are particularly likely to occur in mixed and broad-leaved forests.

Survey methods

As sightings are rare, surveys involve a walk-over survey to identify field signs including dreys, droppings and feeding remains.

Surveys can be undertaken all year round, but the best time is in spring and summer when activity is at its peak. At least some surveys should be undertaken between March and May and/or July and September to identify breeding dens.

Each survey period will take at least several days, depending on the area to be covered. Periods of harsh weather should be avoided.

Depending on the survey methods used, surveyors may require a survey and monitoring licence from the relevant SNCO.

WHAT IF RED SQUIRRELS ARE FOUND ON SITE AFTER WORKS HAVE STARTED?

If a red squirrel or its shelter is found (or suspected) on site after works have started, *works in the area must stop immediately*, as it is an offence to injure, kill, capture or disturb red squirrels, or to damage places they use for shelter or protection. Consult an expert.

Works may need to be delayed until mitigation can be conducted at the appropriate time of year.

Mitigation for red squirrels

If impacts on red squirrels or their habitat cannot be avoided, mitigation measures will be required. Mitigation will depend on the type and scale of the impact.

The following guidance is for general information only. Mitigation must always be designed and conducted on a case-by-case basis and in consultation with an expert. All works and mitigation proposals must be agreed with the relevant SNCO (see Licensing section for details of licensing for tree felling).

- **Vegetation clearance** should be conducted only once mitigation measures have been agreed. Before starting any work, the area should be checked by a specialist who should also be present while clearance work is being carried out.

- **Tree felling, branch-cutting** and **construction works** within red squirrel habitat should be conducted outside of the breeding season, between August and November, wherever possible. The area should also be checked beforehand, as squirrels may remain in their dreys at this time. Clear-felling of continuous swathes of tree cover should be avoided. Instead, felling should be selective.

- **Trees containing dreys** should be marked clearly and left unfelled. Tree felling around these trees must be conducted carefully so that the trees containing dreys are left undamaged. Generally, destruction of red squirrel breeding sites should be avoided at all costs.

- **Hazel and hawthorn** should be left in the understorey as feeding sites.

Other mitigation measures for impacts on red squirrel habitat may include:

■ artificial dreys and rope-bridges

■ maintenance of habitat corridors

■ planting of food plants and new woodland

■ post-construction monitoring.

Positive impacts through development

Incorporating the following measures as part of landscaping can also benefit to the conservation of red squirrels in the UK:

■ planting of tree species that favour red squirrels over grey squirrels, such as Norway spruce, Scots pine, oak, beech and horse chestnut

■ installation of rope bridges (a length of thick rope – such as that used for mooring ships – placed between two trees or telegraph poles high above the road) to allow squirrels to cross roads safely

■ installation of road signs to alert drivers to red squirrels.

The provision of red squirrel feeders is not recommended, as this can lead to a dependency of red squirrel populations on artificial feeding. In addition, feeders have been linked to the spread of parapox disease among red squirrel populations.

Specialist advice should always be sought on a case-by-case basis before carrying out any of the above measures.

Where to go for further help and guidance

Organisations that can be contacted for expert advice on red squirrels:

● wildlife trusts

● The Mammal Society

● SNCOs.

Water vole

WHAT DO THEY LOOK LIKE?

Water voles (*Arvicola terrestris*) are often confused with brown rats because of their similar appearance and their occurrence near water. However, water voles do not pose the same threats to human health as rats.

Natural history

Water voles are active mainly within 2–5 m of the water's edge. They live and breed in

burrows along the banks of watercourses.

Water voles do not hibernate, but are less active above ground during the winter.

Habitat requirements

Water voles are found in both rural and urban areas in England, Wales and Scotland, but do not occur in NI.

Habitats used by the water vole include slow-flowing rivers, streams, ditches, dykes, the edges of lakes, reed-beds, marshes and ponds, with plenty of vegetation both along the bank, in the shallows and in mid-water

Legal protection

It is an offence to disturb sheltering water voles or to damage, destroy or obstruct places they use for shelter or protection.

Ideal water vole habitat includes ditches, marshes and other wetlands with well-layered vegetation

Why do they need special protection?

- in the UK, water voles have undergone a catastrophic 90 per cent decline over the last 50 years.

- this decline is due to habitat loss and predation by the introduced American mink.

Water voles are protected under the **Wildlife and Countryside Act 1981 (Amendment 1998)**, making it an offence to:

- intentionally or recklessly disturb, destroy or obstruct access to any place that water voles use for shelter or protection, eg a burrow (whether occupied or not)

- intentionally or recklessly disturb water voles while they are in a place of shelter or protection.

Following a review of the **Wildlife and Countryside Act** in September 2002, it has been proposed that the water vole should receive *full* legal protection. The most recent versions of the legislation should be consulted.

Other legislation and nature conservation guidance

Water voles that have been captured are protected by UK animal welfare legislation, including the **Wild Mammals Protection Act** which prohibits cruelty and abandonment.

The water vole is identified as a priority species under the *UK Biodiversity Action Plan*.

Licensing for development

The EA or SEPA must be consulted wherever works affect watercourses or wetlands. In many cases, consent will be required before works can go ahead.

There is no provision for SNCOs to issue licences permitting development or maintenance works affecting water voles. In order to avoid prosecution, it must be shown that all reasonable effort was made to avoid breaking the law. This requires evidence of adequate surveys and mitigation. As they are not a European Protected Species there is no requirement for Defra, SEERAD or the WA to issue a licence.

Surveys and mitigation

Wherever development will impact on habitat that may be used by water voles, surveys must be conducted by a specialist. Only once it is confirmed that no water voles are present, can works proceed (as long as any other restrictions have been satisfied).

Surveys are generally not recommended between November and February, as reduced activity means that water voles may be overlooked. For small scale works, however, it may be possible to carry out initial surveys for burrows in the winter months.

Mitigation

- where water voles are shown to be present, SNCOs require that impacts are avoided where at all possible, leaving riparian vegetation intact, either through the use of alternative sites or redesign of the works. Where impacts are completely unavoidable, mitigation measures will need to be agreed and set in place before works go ahead. Generally, all works in water vole habitat, including mitigation, should be undertaken in March, April or August/September if at all possible. However, water vole activity periods, and therefore optimum work periods, vary regionally

- mitigation works may take many weeks or months to complete and in some cases may continue for several years

- the timing of mitigation must take other protected species on site into consideration – for example, clearance of vegetation along watercourses may affect otters, fish and nesting birds.

The works described below must be carried out only under the guidance of an experienced water vole specialist and with the agreement of EN, CCW or SNH. Refer to table on pages 34–36 for details of the timing of mitigation.

Exclusion of water voles

Where habitat loss is completely unavoidable, it may be necessary for water voles to be excluded either temporarily or permanently. Exclusion works may involve vegetation clearance within, and adjacent to, the proposed works area to encourage water voles to leave an area naturally. In some circumstances a trapping programme may be undertaken to remove water voles from an area.

These works should be avoided during the winter months when water voles are less mobile and therefore more vulnerable to injury and less likely to evacuate their burrows.

Before clearing any vegetation, all burrows within the area will need to be identified, checked and marked. Burrows will need to remain open to enable animals to escape.

Cleared areas may need to be left for up to five days, to allow time for water voles to leave the area. Regular checks of burrows should be made by a water vole specialist throughout this period and re-cutting of vegetation may be required.

To prevent water voles from returning to the area of works, exclusion fencing may be needed in the form of wooden plyboards driven down into the bank to water level.

Plyboards installed along a watercourse to prevent watervoles from returning to an area from which they have been excluded

Following completion of works to exclude water voles, burrows must be hand-dug by a water vole specialist to ensure that no animals remain.

Where disturbance is temporary, once works are completed, areas should be replanted or allowed to recolonise with vegetation so that there is no permanent loss of water vole habitat.

Habitat creation

Where areas are to be permanently lost, compensation will need to be made through habitat creation, preferably within adjacent areas. Translocation of animals to other areas should be avoided where at all possible.

The following may be required as mitigation and can also be included in general landscaping to enhance areas for water voles:

- creation of reed beds

- planting of dense vegetation along watercourses

- creation of groups of ponds, ditches and other wetlands

- restoration of ditches to link wetlands together

- fencing of banks to allow natural regeneration

- re-profiling of steep-sided ditches to provide shelves at the water's edge and to promote vegetation buffer strips along watercourses.

What if water voles are found on site after works have started?

If water voles or evidence of their being present on site are found after works have started, **works in the area must stop immediately,** as it is an offence to disturb sheltering water voles, or to damage or obstruct their burrows. Consult an expert for advice on how to proceed.

Works may need to be delayed until mitigation can be conducted at the appropriate time of year.

Essential vegetation clearance and maintenance works

The following are examples of good practice in relation to watercourse management. Specific guidance must always be obtained from the Environment Agency, SEPA and the relevant SNCO.

- all works on water vole habitat, including routine maintenance, should preferably be conducted during March/April, when adults are active but do not yet have young, or August/September, when population numbers are highest and at their most resilient

- clearance works should be phased in order to avoid disturbing all shoreline vegetation at the same time. This can be achieved through:

  - not clearing both banks simultaneously with at least one third of the shoreline left completely untouched

  - cutting vegetation in alternate 50 metre sections (with intervening sections left uncut)

  - wherever possible, leaving a fringe of vegetation along the water's edge.

- bank-side vegetation should be retained and/or re-planted wherever possible

- de-silting or dredging should not interfere with bank sides and should follow the above guidelines.

Differentiating water voles and rats

Feature	Water vole	Brown rat
Appearance	Chestnut brown fur, blunt nose and round face, short rounded ears hidden by fur. Shorter tail.	Brown or black fur, pointed face and prominent eyes and ears. Long, thick hairless tail.
Droppings	Dark green droppings form platforms/piles of droppings.	Light brown droppings scattered in groups.
Burrows and runways	Holes within 2.5 m of water's edge, near or below water-line. "Lawns" of grazed vegetation around burrows.	Rat burrows have a fan of excavated soil and are joined by well-worn "rat-runs".
Behaviour	Mainly active during the day. Shy, rarely seen, hear "plop" as they disappear into water.	Mostly nocturnal but less cautious and more likely to be seen.

Where to go for further help and guidance

Organisations that can be contacted for expert advice on water voles:

- **The Environment Agency or Scottish Environmental Protection Agency**
- **wildlife trusts**
- **SNCOs**

THE WATER VOLE YEAR

Key	
	Reduced activity
	Breeding

Month	J	F	M	A	M	J	J	A	S	O	N	D
Activity												

White-clawed crayfish

WHAT DO THEY LOOK LIKE?

There are six species of freshwater crayfish in the UK, five of which are non-native, ie have been introduced. The species are the red swamp, noble, spiny-cheek, signal, narrow-clawed (Turkish) and white-clawed crayfish.

Only the white-clawed crayfish (*Austropotamobius pallipes*) – also known as the Atlantic stream crayfish – is native to the UK.

Habitat requirements – where are white-clawed crayfish found?

White-clawed crayfish are most abundant in north and central England. They also occur in eastern Wales and a few areas in Northern Ireland and have been introduced to Scotland. Their distribution is patchy in the south of England.

Populations can be very localised to specific sections of a watercourse, making them highly vulnerable should works be carried out within these sections.

White-clawed crayfish can be found in streams, rivers and lakes, canals, gravel and chalk pits, ponds and quarry pools.

The white-clawed crayfish likes clean rivers and lakes with limited sediment and plenty of shelter

Ideal habitat features include:

- submerged tree roots

- bank undercuts

- accumulated debris ("dams")

- crevices in stonework or wooden structures

- stands of submerged and emergent aquatic vegetation

- bank-side vegetation of shrubs and trees, particularly alder, willow and hazel.

Legal protection

- *"Taking" or capture of white-clawed crayfish is an offence unless done under a conservation licence.* Because crayfish spend the daytime sheltering among boulders, tree roots and in crevices (including man-made structures such as gabion baskets, bridges and walls) "taking" can very easily occur during engineering or routine maintenance works on watercourses and associated structures and vegetation.

Details of the legislation are as follows:

Under the **Wildlife and Countryside Act 1981 *(as amended)*** it is an offence to *intentionally take (ie capture), sell, barter or exchange* white-clawed crayfish.

In Northern Ireland white-clawed crayfish receive no protection as yet, though it has been proposed for addition to *Schedule 5* of the **Wildlife (NI) Order 1985**. Recent versions of the relevant legislation should be consulted.

Controlled waters (rivers, streams, canals, groundwaters, coastal and territorial waters) are protected against pollution under the **Water Resources Act 1991**. Under this Act and the **Land Drainage Act 1991**, any works within 8 m of a main river bank or flood-bank, or works that affect flow in any watercourse, require formal consent from the EA, SEPA or EHS-EP(NI).

Under the **Habitats Regulations 1994**, special areas of conservation (SACs) have been designated for the white-clawed crayfish. Works within these areas must be agreed with the relevant SNCO.

Non-native crayfish species

There are five introduced species of crayfish in the UK. Three of these are listed as *"non-native species"* under the **Wildlife and Countryside Act 1981**. These are:

- Signal crayfish

- Turkish crayfish

- Noble crayfish.

If any of these species is captured (eg during engineering works) it is an offence to release them into the wild. Notify the EA, SEPA or EHS-EP(NI).

Other legislation and nature conservation guidance

White-clawed crayfish that have been captured are protected against cruelty (**Protection of Animals Act 1911**; **Welfare of Animals Act (NI) 1972**).

The white-clawed crayfish is classed as "globally threatened" by IUCN/WCMC and is listed as a priority species under the UK Biodiversity Action Plan (BAP). The EA is the lead partner and point of contact for this species.

Licensing for development

The EA, SEPA or EHS-EP(NI) must be consulted wherever works affect watercourses or wetlands. Consents may be required.

A **conservation licence** should be obtained from EN, SNH, CCW or EHS-NH(NI) before conducting any development works that could impact on white-clawed crayfish.

Conservation licences can be granted as long as a development activity is *"properly planned and executed and thereby contributes to the conservation of the population"*.

A conservation licence to capture white-clawed crayfish and remove them from a site will be granted only to a suitably-experienced person and then only if there is evidence of adequate surveys and mitigation plans. Licences take 15 days or more to be granted.

Surveys

Survey methods

Wherever habitat that is suitable for white-clawed crayfish is to be affected, surveys must be undertaken by a suitably-experienced specialist. See table on pages 34–36 for timing.

WHAT IF WHITE-CLAWED CRAYFISH ARE FOUND ON SITE AFTER WORKS HAVE STARTED?

Crayfish may occur at low densities and, even after surveys have been conducted, individuals may still be found unexpectedly. Works on watercourses should therefore proceed with caution.

If a white-clawed crayfish is found on site after works have started, *works in the area must stop immediately*. Consult an expert for advice on how to proceed.

Works may need to be delayed until mitigation can be conducted at the appropriate time of year.

If there is any doubt about which species has been found, works must stop until its identity can be confirmed.

Examples of works that have been identified as potentially affecting white-clawed crayfish are listed in the box below. The full list can be found in *Guidance on works affecting white-clawed crayfish* published by English Nature and the Environment Agency (June 2000).

Receptor sites for crayfish will need to be selected and prepared in advance of any crayfish removals. Capture and removal of crayfish must be carried out only by licensed persons.

Apart from during crayfish surveys, machinery and personnel should not have access to the watercourse until the crayfish rescue is completed.

Additional mitigation measures may include:

- re-scheduling the works to avoid times of low activity and key breeding periods
- habitat improvements and/or re-instatement
- buffer zones along watercourses
- fencing of banks to allow natural regeneration.

Mitigation

Where impacts are completely unavoidable, mitigation measures will need to be agreed and set in place before works go ahead. The timing of mitigation works may be restricted, for instance removal (ie rescue) of crayfish should be conducted only from July to October. See table, pages 34–36. The timing of mitigation must take other protected species into account – eg water vole and otter.

Mitigation works may take many weeks or months to complete and in some cases may continue over several years.

The key guidance on white-clawed crayfish is as follows.

- SNCOs advise that maintenance or engineering works on watercourses that contain white-clawed crayfish are avoided where at all possible.

- Crayfish should be kept in their original watercourse wherever possible, but depending on the scale and type of works it may be necessary to remove white-clawed crayfish from the area of disturbance, either temporarily or permanently.

Why do they need special protection?

- The white-clawed crayfish is the only species of freshwater crayfish native to the UK.

- It has undergone widespread decline due to inappropriate river management, pollution and the spread of a fungal disease know as "crayfish plague" following the introduction of non-native species (particularly in the south).

- White-clawed crayfish have a low reproductive rate and are slow to recover from population losses.

Examples of works that can potentially affect white-clawed crayfish

- disturbance of river banks, eg removal of habitat used for sheltering such as boulders and bank-side vegetation, fallen trees and branches, leaf litter etc
- disturbance of channel bed such as dredging or surfacing (eg around outfalls)
- removal of bank-side vegetation (coppicing should be used as an alternative)
- de-watering operations, including drainage of construction sites
- re-inforcement and re-profiling of river banks with concrete channels, sheet-piling, revetting, removal of established debris dams (eg for flood defence)
- installation or re-installation of gabions (crayfish may shelter within baskets)
- construction and repair of structures such as bridges, outfalls, walls, pipeline crossings, aqueducts, canal wash-walls, weirs, locks and sluices
- channel diversions
- permanent removal of riverside stock fencing
- indirect effects such as siltation from run-off, pollution from oil, fuel, livestock.

All of the above works should be carried out under specialist guidance.

When planning and designing works, consideration should be given to the fact that many of these activities can impact on areas well beyond the actual site of works. Impacts on areas up- and down-stream should be taken into account and discussed with the EA, SEPA or EHS-EP(NI).

A settlement lagoon to prevent run-off from construction works polluting existing watercourses

Crayfish plague

Crayfish plague is carried by the introduced signal crayfish and can completely eliminate populations of white-clawed crayfish within weeks. The disease can be carried on wet vehicles and survey equipment.

Measures must be taken to prevent the spread of crayfish disease to adjacent watercourses that contain white-clawed crayfish populations, eg via drainage of infected water or transport of non-native species.

Some general advice on how to avoid spreading the disease is listed below.

- Work progressively downstream wherever possible.
- If moving between sites, always carry out works first on the watercourses that contain white-clawed crayfish.
- Following works in watercourses that contain non-native crayfish species, disinfect all equipment – or at the very least ensure it is thoroughly cleaned and dried.
- Do not stock watercourses with plants or fish from watercourses containing non-native crayfish.

The potential of any watercourse to support white-clawed crayfish may be improved by following the guidelines below.

- Avoid siltation, locally or downstream.
- Use coarse sediment such as gravel and large stones for re-surfacing works.
- Create refuges for crayfish (and other species) within hard-bank reinforcement by leaving unmortared crevices, holes and by inserting short sections of pipe.
- Create new water bodies.
- Plant appropriate vegetation along watercourses to provide shelter and leaf debris on which crayfish feed.
- Coppice trees, rather than removing stumps.
- Use gabion baskets as these can provide good sheltering habitat for crayfish, but care must be taken to avoid loss of animals when replacing or removing gabions.

THE WHITE-CLAWED CRAYFISH YEAR

	Key
	Peak numbers
	Moderate numbers
	Few individuals

Month	J	F	M	A	M	J	J	A	S	O	N	D
Adults active												

Natterjack toad

WHAT DO THEY LOOK LIKE?

In comparison to the common toad (*Bufo bufo*), the natterjack toad (*Bufo calamita*) is smaller and has a distinctive narrow yellow stripe running along the length of its back (young toadlets also have this stripe). The background colour is grey-brown to dark olive-green and they have a warty skin.

An adult natterjack toad is approximately 75 mm long.

The natterjack has a distinctive, metallic sounding croak. They are mostly active at night, but will also occasionally come out during the day.

Unlike frogs, which lay clumps of eggs, toads tend to produce a string of eggs. Natterjack toad strings have a single row of black eggs, while those of the common toad have a double row.

Natural history

Natterjack toads breed in ephemeral ponds, but spend most of their time on land, foraging and sheltering.

Adults can be found breeding in pools from *April to August*, and tadpoles may be found from *May to early September*.

Females lay approximately 1500 eggs, which hatch after seven to 10 days. After four to eight weeks, tadpoles change into the adult form and leave the ponds. Young natterjacks may be as small as 7 mm.

Natterjack habitat includes sand dunes, coastal grazing marshes and heaths

Both adults and juveniles can also be found on land at any time of year. In winter they dig deep underground tunnels where they hibernate from October to March or early April.

Habitat requirements

Natterjack toads are found predominantly in sandy habitats such as coastal sand dunes and grazing marshes or lowland heaths. In Cumbria and Scotland populations are also thriving on upland moor, salt marshes and post-industrial sites.

The natterjack toad competition prefers shallow ponds, where it faces less competition from the common toad and where invertebrate predator numbers are kept low due to seasonal desiccation. It may also be found in large ponds or small lakes with shallow margins, where fish such as perch or carp keep the number of other invertebrate predators low, but find the natterjack's tadpoles distasteful.

Legal protection

Because it is so rare, the natterjack and parts of its habitat are fully protected under the *Wildlife and Countryside Act 1981,* and the *Habitats Regulations 1994).* It is an offence to:

Why do they need special protection?

- *The natterjack is now confined only to a handful of carefully monitored sites in the UK.* Re-introduction programmes are being implemented to help halt its decline.

- They occur naturally in England and at four sites in Scotland and have been introduced to sites in Wales. They are found in south-west Ireland but not in Northern Ireland.

- The natterjack is almost exclusively confined to coastal sand dune systems, coastal grazing marshes and sandy heaths.

- They occur on sites in Merseyside, Cumbria and Solway and in low numbers in Surrey, Hampshire and East Anglia, Dorset and Bedfordshire.

- ■ intentionally or deliberately capture, kill or injure natterjack toads

- ■ intentionally, deliberately or recklessly* damage, destroy or obstruct access to any place used for breeding, resting, shelter or protection (occupied or not)

- ■ deliberately, intentionally or recklessly* disturb natterjack toads when in a place of shelter

- ■ sell, barter, exchange or transport or offer for sale natterjack toads or parts of them.

The legislation covers all life stages: eggs, tadpoles, juveniles and adults.

* For England and Wales, the term "reckless" was added as an amendment to the **Wildlife and Countryside Act 1981** as a result of the **CRoW Act 2000**.

Other legislation and nature conservation guidance

Toads that have been captured are protected by UK animal welfare legislation, which prohibits cruelty and abandonment (**Protection of Animals Act, 1911**; **Abandonment of Animals Act, 1960**).

The natterjack toad is listed as a priority species under the UK Biodiversity Action Plan and re-introduction programmes have been established in some parts of the country.

Licensing for development

Before undertaking any development or mitigation works that will affect natterjack toads or their habitat, a development licence must first be obtained from DEFRA, SEERAD or the WA. This will be granted only to a suitably-qualified person and will depend on evidence of adequate surveys and mitigation plans.

Surveys and mitigation

The EA or SEPA must be consulted wherever works affect watercourses or wetlands. Consents may be required.

The majority of natterjack toad populations are already documented and most are contained within SSSIs or nature reserves. However, surveys are likely to be required where development impacts on areas in the vicinity of known populations.

Surveys must be undertaken only by people who are suitably trained and experienced in recognising natterjack toads. Surveyors may require a personal surveying licence (obtained from EN, CCW, SNH) as disturbance or capture is an offence without an appropriate licence and most survey methods will involve some level of disturbance.

Survey methods

Surveys may involve night-time searches for adults on land and in pools using torchlight, refugia searches, listening for toad-calls, searching for spawn signs, netting of tadpoles and counting emerging toadlets.

Spawn counts are often the best method for establishing population size, but only if repeated on a frequent basis.

Surveys for adults are undertaken at night, while spawn, tadpoles and toadlets can be surveyed during the day.

WHAT IF NATTERJACK TOADS ARE FOUND ON SITE AFTER WORKS HAVE STARTED?

If natterjack toads are found (or suspected) on site after works have started, *works in the area must stop immediately*, as it is illegal to injure, kill, capture or disturb natterjacks, or to damage their sheltering place, without a development licence. Advice must be sought from an experienced ecologist and EN, SNH or CCW. Works may need to be delayed until mitigation can be conducted at the appropriate time of year.

Keeping within the law

To enable appropriate time-tabling of development works on sites where natterjack toads may be present, the following three points should be considered:

1   Generally, pond surveys can be conducted only during April, May and June. Surveys of terrestrial natterjack habitat are restricted due to inactivity of toads during spells of dry weather. No surveys can be undertaken between October and February/early March.

2   Where natterjack toads are shown to be present, SNCOs require that impacts are avoided where at all possible, either through the use of alternative sites or redesign of the works. Where impacts are completely unavoidable, mitigation measures will need to be agreed and set in place before works go ahead. The timing of mitigation works may be restricted, for instance capture programmes in ponds can be undertaken only between April and June, and capture on land is restricted to April to September (excluding hot and dry periods).

3   To avoid prosecution under the Wildlife and Countryside Act 1981 (as amended) and the Habitats Regulations 1994, wherever works will impact on natterjack toads a development licence must be obtained before any mitigation or other works begin. Licences can take up to 30 days or more to be granted.

Mitigation for natterjack toads

The natterjack toad is extremely rare and is subject to re-introduction measures to increase its range. It is therefore considered unlikely that development would be permitted on a site holding one of the few remaining natterjack toad populations.

If, however, a proposed development is to impact on natterjack toads, mitigation will be required to compensate for the effects of the development. Any mitigation proposals for natterjack toads must be designed and conducted under expert guidance and in consultation with the relevant SNCO.

Once an appropriate mitigation and monitoring strategy has been designed and where necessary agreed with the EA, SEPA, EN, CCW or SNH, a development licence must be obtained from Defra, the WA or SEERAD, *to allow mitigation works to be started in advance of development works.*

Creation of new habitat for natterjack toad

Mitigation measures, as advance works, may include exclusion of toads from work areas, translocation to a safe area, creation of new ponds and suitable terrestrial habitat. It may also be necessary to change the timing of some construction operations.

Translocation of natterjack toads

Translocation should be regarded only as a last resort, not just for the natterjack toad, but for all protected species. Where a pond or an area of land where natterjack toads occur is to be lost, it may be necessary to move animals into a safe area. This would be possible only between April and September.

Creating new habitat

Any loss of habitat, including both ponds and terrestrial habitat, must be compensated for through habitat creation.

New ponds can be created by hand or using machinery. They should be shallow and with gradually shelving edges. Excavation spoil can be used to create terrestrial habitat in the form of south-facing banks near the pond.

Ponds should be created at least 12 months before they are to be used by the toads.

Provision of sluices in sea walls

If sea wall construction will prevent inundation of saltmarsh ponds at high tide it may be necessary to create sluices in the walls as and where appropriate, to maintain connectivity and hydrological integrity.

All of these works must be undertaken only under the guidance of a suitably-experienced, licenced specialist.

Positive impacts through development

Development can also offer the chance to provide additional habitat for the natterjack toad as part of landscaping, for example through:

- restoration of sand dune habitat
- creation of groups of shallow pools with gradually shelving margins
- tree and scrub clearance, creating more suitable habitat for natterjack toads.

Where to go for further help and guidance

Organisations that can be contacted for expert advice on natterjack toads:

- **SNCOs**
- **The Herpetological Conservation Trust**
- **The British Herpetological Society**
- **Froglife**

Feral pigeon

WHAT ARE THEY AND HOW DO I RECOGNISE THEM?

- The feral pigeon (*Columbo livia*) is derived from the native rock dove and is now found in large flocks in urban areas throughout the UK.

- They are usually bluish- grey with a white rump and darker-coloured wings and often have purple-green patches on neck and breast.

- Pigeons build their nests in or on roofs, lofts, building or monument ledges, bridge supports, air conditioning units and window sills.

- Their nests are a simple platform of twigs, grasses or scraps such as plastic and wire.

What do I do if I have pigeons on site?

Nests can be found at any time of year. *Pigeon control measures and removal of pigeon droppings should be carried only out by specialist contractors.*

Without a "general licence", it is illegal to kill, injure or take feral pigeons or destroy their eggs or nest.

Removal of nests and other pest control measures are illegal if they impact on protected species, for example non-pest species of breeding birds or bats.

Health and safety issues and pest control methods

- Feral pigeons and their droppings can transmit diseases to humans and domestic animals. Some of these are potentially fatal!

- Fouling of pathways can make walkways slippery.

- Killing pigeons is unlikely to be effective, as more pigeons quickly move in from neighbouring areas. The most effective deterrent is to remove food sources. Do not provide food and use secure storage for food waste and refuse on site.

- Pigeons may be prevented from entering or roosting on buildings by using netting or wire mesh. But note that this action will be illegal if it impacts on bats and may also have a detrimental impact on other bird species. Consult an ecologist for advice before blocking access to roofs and buildings.

- Pest control methods must be implemented only by a registered pest control company – many methods are subject to legal restrictions and may be illegal if they impact on protected species of wildlife. A general licence may be required – See species notes on birds p65.

- Do not handle pigeon droppings without wearing protective equipment.

Foxes

WHAT ARE THEY AND HOW DO I RECOGNISE THEM?

Foxes (*Vulpes vulpes*) are the size of a medium-sized dog and have reddish orange fur with a bushy tail.

- they are slim in build with a long pointed snout

- fox droppings are similar to those of domestic dogs but are twisted in shape, often contain hair and bones and have a pungent smell.

Where might I expect to find them?

Foxes occur in nearly all habitats including agricultural land, woodland, coastal and mountain areas and urban areas.

They occupy underground dens called "earths" – which may be shared with other species including protected animals such as badgers.

Health and safety issues

- foxes may carry Weil's disease (*Leptospirosis*), which can be passed on to humans via fox urine
- foxes (like dogs) carry parasites that can cause disease in humans, passed on via droppings.

Avoid contact with fox urine or droppings (or any standing water that may be contaminated) with bare hands!

What do I do if I find one?

Cruelty to foxes and the use of poison and certain types of trap to capture them are illegal.

Works affecting fox dens:

- avoid destruction of fox dens until sure that foxes have evacuated

- foxes bred during March – May, at which time cubs will be in dens underground

- to avoid breaking the laws protecting animals against cruelty, only lightly fill holes at first to avoid burying any animals and to detect whether the hole is in use. Use leaf litter or straw rather than soil

- foxes may use badger holes! It is an offence to damage badger holes without a licence. If in doubt as to whether a hole is used by a badger, stop all works and consult an expert.

Grey squirrels

WHAT ARE THEY AND HOW DO I RECOGNISE THEM?

Grey squirrels (*Sciurus carolinensis*) are up to 300 mm long plus a long bushy tail.

Red squirrel

- their fur is grey with a brown or reddish tint in places and may be mistaken for red squirrels, though red squirrels are much redder, and are now quite rare in the UK

- grey squirrels are slightly larger than red squirrels, their ears are more rounded and they don't usually have the long pointy ear tufts red squirrels have. The most obvious difference is the colour of their fur

Grey squirrel

- **grey squirrels are an introduced species and are not protected.** *Red squirrels are rare and strictly protected in the UK.*

Where might I expect to find them?

Grey squirrels occur in a wide range of habitats, from rural deciduous and mixed woodland and hedgerow to urban parks, gardens and roadsides. They are often seen on the ground and in trees.

- nests are built among the branches of large trees, away from the main trunk, and also in roof spaces of buildings

- squirrel nests or "dreys" are round and compact, made of twigs and leaves, and may be mistaken for birds' nests.

Measures used to control grey squirrels will be illegal if they impact on any other protected species, ie red squirrels or bats or nesting birds. Seek expert advice.

> **What do I do if I find one?**
>
> - Unlike the grey squirrel, the *red squirrel* is *strictly protected* in the UK and any works that impact on it are illegal without a licence.
>
> - If in any doubt as to whether what you have found is a grey or a red squirrel, or whether a nest is used by birds, stop all works immediately, and consult an expert.
>
> - Although not protected against killing, injury or disturbance, grey squirrels are protected against cruelty, as are all wild mammals.

Invasive plants

WHAT ARE INVASIVE PLANTS?

Some plants are so invasive that they have become a problem, particularly to our native flora.

Legal situation

Section 14(2) of the **Wildlife and Countryside Act 1981** prohibits the planting of certain species in the wild or otherwise causing them to grow there. Prohibited plants are listed on Part II of *Schedule 9*, and include **Japanese knotweed** (*Polygonum cuspidatum*) and **giant hogweed** (*Heracleum mantegazzianum*).

- It is not an offence to have these plants growing on your land or land that you have an interest in.

- It is an offence to plant or otherwise to cause these species to grow in the wild. In effect this means that if they are growing on your site and there is danger of construction-related activities spreading them, either within or without the project area, then it is essential to put measures in place to stop this from happening.

It is the responsibility of the contractors to ensure that they are aware of their legal responsibilities in dealing with Japanese knotweed, particularly in respect of the use of herbicides and the disposal of knotweed rhizomes.

Contact with the EA, SEPA or EHS-EP(NI) is strongly recommended.

The three main culprits: giant hogweed, Himalayan balsam and Japanese knotweed

Young knotweed plants growing in concrete – possibly spread through careless handling of contaminated material

- Some native species of plant, common ragwort for example, can cause problems for farmers, horse-owners or other neighbours of development projects and are termed notifiable weeds under the **Weeds Act 1959**. You may be required to control these plants.

Japanese knotweed is extremely vigorous and once established is difficult to eradicate. It is easily spread to new areas by earth moving or disposal of cut waste.

In the winter it is not visible above ground although the dead stems, which resemble a reddish brown bamboo, are often obvious. In the spring it emerges and by the summer has normally achieved a height of 2–3 m. The leaves are shaped like a shield with a small pointed tip and are bright green, though are often reddish when they first emerge.

Giant hogweed can take four years to flower, but when it does so it is unmistakable – up to 5 metres tall and with large umbels of flowers on top of each stem, rather like a giant version of cow parsley. It produces poisonous sap that can blister skin.

Survey

A pre-construction survey should be undertaken by an experienced botanist for Japanese knotweed, giant hogweed and other invasive species. Any plants should be accurately plotted on a map and described in a report. Copies should provided to all relevant staff.

Other troublesome plants

Common ragwort (*Senecio jacobaea*) is a common and widespread native biennial plant found throughout much of the UK. It is poisonous to horses and other livestock, and in situations where such animals are present it is advisable to control it. It is a notifiable injurious weed under the **Weeds Act 1959**. In relation to construction sites, it may not be possible or necessary to eradicate it, but it may be necessary to prevent its spread to neighbouring land, which it does by shedding copious amounts of seed. This can be achieved either through cutting, hand pulling or treatment with herbicide. Dead plant material should be burned or bagged up and disposed of to landfill as it may still shed seed and can still be poisonous to livestock.

In 2004 Defra published a "Code of Practice on how to prevent spread of Ragwort." The guide states that where common ragwort (is present, every occupier of land should take reasonable measures to prevent it spreading to neighbouring land. However, it also recognises that common ragwort and other ragwort species are an inherent part of our flora and fauna and support invertebrates and other species of wildlife.

Himalayan balsam (*Impatiens glandulifera*) is a native of the Himalayas and grows up to three metres in height. It has spread rapidly throughout the British Isles since being introduced in the nineteenth century. It occurs in damp habitats alongside rivers and streams. It shades out other waterside vegetation and, because it dies back in winter, leaves banks exposed to erosion. It can be controlled by regular cutting, grazing or by using herbicides.

Controlling giant hogweed on site

- the best method of control is a combination of physical and chemical techniques. Before embarking on any control programme the operative should be well protected from any sap – overalls, gloves and a facemask are recommended

- if the plant is noticed before it has set seed a programme of spraying with a glyphosate-based herbicide is recommended. Further applications may be necessary at four-week intervals to ensure effectiveness or to kill any new growth

- if the plant has set seed but not yet dropped it, then the seed head can be removed by cutting it off and placing it in a bag, trying as far as possible to avoid any spillage of material on to the ground. This should be carried out only if protective clothing is being worn and the operatives are confident in what they are doing. Once the seeds have been bagged up they should be burned. The rest of the plant can be treated with glyphosate as above.

A young giant hogweed plant

Controlling Japanese knotweed on site

- on locating Japanese knotweed each discrete clump should be fenced off at a minimum of 3.5 metres radius all around the outermost stems of the plant. The fencing should preferably be chestnut paling and signposted with appropriate wording (eg "Japanese knotweed – do not move soils or material from this site without written approval of the environment manager Tel. No:..."). All appropriate staff should be advised both verbally and in writing (eg site environmental manager, foremen, earthworks contractor, project manager, site engineers)

A Japanese knotweed burial pit

- if the land that is contaminated with knotweed is not required for construction purposes or is not in danger of being tracked over or affected by construction works in any way, it may be safest to leave the plant alone. It is not an offence to leave it growing, *in-situ*, only to spread it to new areas

- if the land that is contaminated with knotweed is required for construction purposes or is in danger of being tracked over or affected by construction works in any way then it must be dealt with in a rigorous and effective way. Failure to do so not only risks prosecution but may result in high costs to eradicate any new growth

- there are two principal mechanisms for eradicating Japanese knotweed: excavation and deep-burial and herbicide treatment.

1 Excavation and burial

The whole plant and its root system should be excavated by machine standing on uncontaminated ground. Excavation should remove:

- vegetation
- topsoil and subsoil to a depth of 3.5 metres and 7 metres diameter around the plant to ensure that all parts of the root system have been removed.

In addition:

- materials should be excavated together and moved to a burial pit in a covered wagon
- storage of contaminated soil should be avoided wherever possible
- tracking over contaminated soils must not be allowed.

Controlling Japanese knotweed on site *(continued)*

- excavated material should be stockpiled within the main work site for continued herbicide treatment, buried on site at a minimum of 5 metres deep (where space and the construction programme allows), or transported to a landfill licensed to take Japanese knotweed for deep burial (contact the EA, SEPA or EHS-EP (NI) for landfill sites that are so licensed)

- where burial takes place on-site the contaminated soil should be covered with an impervious barrier (eg geotextile or heavy gauge polythene), before being backfilled

- all machinery should be cleaned off into the burial pit or on to a designated clean-off area lined with geotextile. In the latter instance this material should be disposed of carefully into the burial pit to ensure no cross contamination. All hand tools and footwear should be cleaned off in a similar manner.

- on-site burial pits should be clearly marked on a plan to enable follow up checks.

2 Herbicide treatment

- plants should be allowed to grow to between 1–1.5 metres tall before being cut back. All cut material should be left *in-situ*.

- once re-growth has attained a height of between 1–1.5 metres it should be sprayed with herbicide to the manufacturers specification

- herbicides that are effective in controlling Japanese knotweed include:

  - Picloram (Tordon 22K)

  - Glyphosate (marketed under names such as Roundup, Tumbleweed etc)

  - or a combination of Picloram (Tordon 22K) and 2,4-D

- Picloram is persistent in the soil for up to two years so should not be used where immediate re-vegetation is required. It is also unsuitable for use in or near water. Near to watercourses a glyphosate-based herbicide should be used

- note that the use of herbicides near watercourses requires consultation with the EA

- knotweed may require several repeat treatments to achieve control

Japanese knotweed growing back after clearance

- all areas where Japanese knotweed has been known to exist, whether sprayed or dug up, should be fenced off and kept clear of any construction activities for as long as possible. No temporary storage of soils or other materials should be allowed on top of old knotweed sites. A watching brief for the reappearance of knotweed should be maintained in these areas.

Consult the website www.netregs.gov.uk for the latest government guidance on controlling Japanese knotweed.

Mink

Mink (*Mustela vison*) are an introduced species that impact on native wildlife. For example, they have been implicated in the catastrophic decline of the water vole. Mink and their dens and droppings may be confused with those of other species such as otters and pine martens, that are strictly protected in the UK.

WHAT ARE THEY AND HOW DO I RECOGNISE THEM?

Mink have a slender body with a long tail and short legs and are similar in size to a ferret or a small cat.

- they have a glossy, dark brown to silver coat with white throat patches
- droppings are left in conspicuous places such as large boulders, tree stumps and close to dens. They are long and thin (up to 80 mm), tightly twisted and smell strongly rancid.

Where might I expect to find them?

Mink live near fresh water that has dense vegetation cover alongside, such as slow-flowing rivers, ponds, marshes and lakes.

They have dens in places such as hollow trees and logs, rabbit burrows and rock crevices.

If you find a hole on site that you suspect is an animal den, stop all works immediately and consult an expert.

What do I do if I find a mink?

Always get expert advice to ensure that the animal (or den) is definitely mink.

Where mink are confirmed as present, control measures may be undertaken. These must by implemented only by a registered pest control company. Contact an ecologist or Defra for more information.

Measures used to control mink will be illegal if they impact on protected species.

Mink, like all wild mammals, are protected against cruelty. Killing animals by filling in dens amounts to cruelty.

Dens or holes found on site may be used by protected species such as badger, water vole, otter or pine marten – so take care.

Rats

WHAT ARE THEY AND HOW DO I RECOGNISE THEM?

Two types of rat are found in the UK: the brown rat and the black rat. Both are introduced (non-native) species.

- the brown rat is the most common and is widespread in urban and rural areas

- the black rat is now confined mainly to London docklands and other port areas

- because they are seen often in or near water, rats are frequently confused with water voles which are protected by UK law.

The table below summarises the differences between rats and water voles.

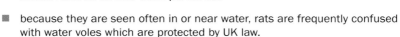

Feature	Brown rat	Water vole
Appearance	Brown or black fur, pointed face and prominent eyes and ears. Long, thick hairless tail.	Chestnut brown fur, blunt nose and round face, short rounded ears hidden by fur. Shorter tail.
Droppings	Light brown droppings scattered in groups.	Dark green droppings form platforms/piles of droppings.
Burrows and runways	Rat burrows have a fan of excavated soil and are joined by well-worn "rat-runs".	Holes within 2.5 m of water's edge, near or below water-line. "Lawns" of grazed vegetation around burrows.
Behaviour	Mostly nocturnal but less cautious and more likely to be seen.	Mainly active during the day. Shy, rarely seen, hear "plop" as they disappear into water.

If in any doubt as to whether what you have found is a rat or a water vole, including burrows, stop all works immediately and consult an expert!

Rats – what to look for

- signs of gnawing on wooden doors etc and burrows in open ground, outbuildings, under floorboards etc

- brown rats live in a wide range of situations, generally close to people (urban areas, refuse tips, sewer systems, farmyards), but are also found in arable fields.

Habitat briefing – coastal & marine habitat

BACKGROUND

Further detail on coastal and marine environmental issues – including ecology – can be found in the CIRIA publication *Coastal and marine environmental site guide* (CIRIA C584, 2003).

Types of coastal and marine habitat

The main types of coastal habitats are:

- estuaries
- mudflats, sandbanks and saltmarshes
- grazing marsh
- coastal lagoons
- shingle beaches and ridges
- sand dunes
- sea cliffs
- marine habitats, eg rocky shore, kelp forest, seagrass beds, cold water reefs.

Legal protection

A wide range of coastal habitats have been awarded protection under the following designations:

- Ramsar
- SPA
- SAC
- NNR
- LNR
- SINC
- MNR
- AONB
- WHS.

Special planning provisions apply on these sites.

Refer to Appendix for details of site designations, legislation and glossary.

Sand dunes may accommodate the natterjack toad and other rare species

Several coastal plants receive legal protection under **Schedule 8** of the **Wildlife and Countryside Act 1981 (as amended)** – see protected plants in the species briefing sheets (old sea walls are the favoured habitat of several of them!).

A number of protected animal species are associated with coastal habitats, including otter, water vole, sand lizard, natterjack toad, a wide range of nesting birds and invertebrates.

Protected species in the marine environment include all cetaceans (whales, dolphins and porpoises), marine turtles, several species of fish including basking shark, and a number of invertebrates.

Grey and common seals are given protection during a close season under the **Conservation of Seals Act 1970**. In Northern Ireland, seals and their habitat are protected at all times.

The **Water Framework Directive** is likely to influence the design and implementation of construction projects that affect inland and coastal waters.

Common seals on a sandbank on the Norfolk coast

Bottle-nosed dolphins off the coast of Scotland

Protecting coastal and marine habitats on site during construction works

- In the case of terrestrial habitats this will usually involve the erection of some form of protective fencing, for example chestnut paling mounted on a scaffold framework. Signs should be erected stating that the area is protected and that there is no access for site vehicles or staff without the permission of the environment manager.

- The protection of inter-tidal or marine features is more difficult but it may be possible to delineate protected areas using flags, buoys and through mapping them accurately using a global positioning system.

- Where appropriate a terrestrial buffer strip should be maintained around the margins of any protected areas, to intercept silt carried in run-off and to protect from other forms of pollution.

- Winds, waves, currents, tides and storms make working in coastal and marine environments more difficult and can profoundly affect whether or not a particular construction activity has any adverse ecological effects. Plan for these factors and be aware of the latest forecasts for weather and tides.

- Drainage or changes in flow into and out of an area can cause irreparable damage .

- Soil and vegetation are susceptible to compaction and other damage (sand dune vegetation for example). In general it is advisable to keep machinery out of any important areas of coastal habitat. Where crossing such an area is unavoidable, try to use low ground pressure machinery and utilise geotextile mats or sleeper mattresses. Rocky shores can be protected to some extent by covering with a layer of sand, with geotextile over the top.

- **Other factors that can cause damage to coastal and marine habitats include the following.**
    - **All forms of pollution, including silt and dust.**
    - **Dredging**
    - **Changes in water chemistry** Care should be taken with choice of materials for haul roads etc (eg avoid limestone in acid areas) and when pumping groundwater into surface waters. Concrete wash-out pits should be carefully located. Avoid inputs of freshwater to brackish and saltwater .
    - **De-watering** in coastal wetlands .
    - **Changes to currents** as a result of temporary or permanent obstructions.
    - **Disturbance**, in the form of noise or the physical presence of people or machinery.
    - **Importation or redistribution of sand, sediment and other materials.**

Grassland

TYPES OF GRASSLAND

Acid grassland
As the name implies, these have developed on acid soils (pH <5.5). Such grasslands are widespread in the uplands and were also formerly common in the lowlands where they were characteristic of free-draining sands and gravels.

Neutral grassland
Neutral grassland occurs on soils that are more or less neutral in reaction (pH 5.5–7) and is typical of lowlands clays and loams.

Calcareous grassland
This occurs on alkaline soils (pH 7 and above) and is largely confined to chalk and limestone outcrops or other situations where the soil contains large amounts of calcium carbonate.

"Improved" and "unimproved" grasslands
A further distinction is that between "improved" and "unimproved" or "semi-improved" grasslands. Those that are of interest to conservationists mainly belong to the "unimproved" or "semi-improved" categories.

Improved grassland has been substantially altered through re-seeding, drainage, and/or fertiliser and herbicide application.

Semi-improved grasslands are those which have received limited agricultural improvement in the past.

Completely **unimproved grasslands** are products of traditional land management carried out by our ancestors over many years and are now very rare. Such grasslands support a rich diversity of grasses and wildflowers. They are therefore very valuable in terms of nature conservation.

Grassland often occurs in mosaic with other habitats, such as scrub or wetland

Good quality grassland habitats are now uncommon and therefore of importance for nature conservation.

Thorpe Meadows – a species-rich neutral grassland

Legal protection

Grasslands may be protected by any of the following:

- SSSI
- ASSI (NI)
- SAC
- SPA.
- NNR
- LNR
- SINC

Some grassland plants receive legal protection in their own right under the *Wildlife and Countryside Act 1981 (as amended)* and, in Northern Ireland, the *Wildlife (NI) Order 1985.*

It is also an offence to uproot any wild plant without the landowner's permission.

Protected animal species that are associated with grassland habitats include reptiles and nesting birds.

Identifying grassland on site

Grassland is generally an easy habitat to identify, but determining precisely what type of grassland it is and whether it has any conservation value requires some ecological experience.

Grassland may be valuable habitat for invertebrates and small mammals or support protected reptiles such as slow-worm and common lizard.

Useful references:

- Anderson, P and Groutage, P. *Habitat translocation – a best practice guide* (CIRIA C600, 2003).

Protecting grassland on site

- Any areas of grassland that are of special conservation value should be identified and protected. This will usually involve the erection of some form of protective fencing such as chestnut paling mounted on a scaffold framework. Signs should be erected stating that the area is protected and that there is no access for site vehicles or staff without the permission of the Environment Manager.

- Grassland habitats may be damaged indirectly by construction activities. They are particularly vulnerable to changes in hydrology (eg through drainage or flooding of an area). Accumulation of silt from run-off is also potentially damaging, as is dust, eg by directly smothering plants.

- In some circumstances it may be possible to provide temporary access across an area of grassland without causing irreparable damage. Laying a protective geotextile blanket over the grassland and covering this with a sleeper trackway or stone sub-base may allow the survival of the turf below , providing that it does not remain covered for too long or that heavy loads do not cause compaction and rutting.

- In exceptional cases it may be possible to translocate grassland to a new site. This requires careful planning and implementation to achieve even a modicum of success.

Heathland

Heathland (or heath) is a vegetation type that is dominated by dwarf shrubs – typically members of the heather family and small species of gorse (there are also other rare types of heath known as lichen or bryophyte heath and grass heath.

Heathland occurs in the lowlands, where it is found on impoverished acid soils such as sands and gravels, and in the uplands, where it is widespread as heather moorland on peat and other acid soils.

Types of heathland:

- wet heath
- dry heath

Conservation status

The area of heathland in the UK has diminished significantly in recent decades. In the lowlands, heathland has come under pressure from urban development, from mineral extraction and from conversion to agricultural land and commercial forestry.

Legal protection

Many of the remaining heathlands are protected under the following designations:

- SSSI
- NNR
- ASSI (NI)
- LNR
- SAC
- SINC
- SPA

Heathland on Exmoor

Some heathland plants receive legal protection making it an offence to intentionally pick, uproot or destroy any of these plants without a licence.

In addition it is an offence to uproot any wild plant without the landowner's permission.

A number of protected animal species are associated with heathland habitats. These include reptiles such as smooth snake and sand lizard, amphibians such as the natterjack toad and birds such as Dartford warbler, nightjar and woodlark.

Protecting heathland on site

- any areas of heathland on site should be identified and protected. This will usually involve the erection of some form of protective fencing such as chestnut paling mounted on a scaffold framework. Signs should be erected stating that the area is protected and that there is no access for site vehicles or staff without the permission of the environment manager

- where protected species such as sand lizard occur other forms of fencing may be necessary to protect the animals and their heathland habitat

- heathland habitats may be directly damaged by construction activities – for example by crushing or trampling – or indirectly. They are particularly vulnerable to changes in hydrology (for example through drainage or flooding of an area)

- accumulation of silt from run-off and dust are also potentially damaging, eg by directly smothering plants. Cement dust and other lime-rich materials are especially damaging as they have the potential to alter the chemistry of the soil

- heathland vegetation is highly flammable during dry periods so great care needs to be taken to prevent accidental fires. A fire control plan should be developed where there are significant areas of heathland on site

- in some circumstances it may be possible to provide temporary access across an area of heathland without causing irreparable damage. Cutting back the vegetation, laying a protective geotextile blanket and covering this with a sleeper trackway or stone sub-base (not concrete, chalk or limestone!) may allow the survival of the heathland vegetation below, providing that it does not remain covered for too long or that heavy loads do not cause compaction and rutting

- in exceptional cases it may be possible to translocate heathland to a new site. However, this is never entirely satisfactory and is no substitute for conservation *in-situ*.

Extensive areas of heathland such as this are now very rare

The smooth snake – one of the reptile species associated with heathland

Useful references:

- Anderson, P and Groutage, P. *Habitat translocation – a best practice guide* (CIRIA C600, 2003).

Hedgerows and individual trees

WHAT ARE THEY?

Hedgerows

Hedgerows are close rows of shrubs or trees serving as a fence or barrier. All can have potential conservation value.

Trees

Any mature tree can provide a valuable habitat, eg for bats. Rare or uncommon tree species are especially valued.

Old parkland trees deserve a special mention – these are often of particular importance to invertebrates; a number of species specialise on dead wood.

All hedges are important, especially where they and their accompanying verges may constitute the only semi-natural habitat for wildlife. They also provide a network of connections to other habitats such as woods and ponds. For example, they can provide important flyways for bats.

Hornbeam grown out of an old hedgerow

It is reckoned that something in excess of 100 000 miles of hedgerow have been lost in the past 40 years, as a result of agricultural intensification and development. There has been an overall decline in non-woodland tree numbers, especially of old native and mature specimens.

Legal protection

In England and Wales hedgerows are protected under the **Hedgerow Regulations 1997**, which require landowners and/or tenants to submit a hedgerow removal notice to the LPA.

- for important hedgerows, LPA will issue a "hedgerow retention notice", requiring the hedge to be preserved

The dormouse will not cross open ground and so relies on hedgerows as "green corridors" between feeding habitats

- it is a criminal offence to remove a hedgerow without submitting a notice to the LPA and waiting for their decision. The regulations do not apply to hedges around private dwellings or where planning permission has been granted for a project that includes hedge removal. (See Appendix tables, page 180, for legislation and implications)

- individual trees (and hedges) can be protected by Tree Preservation Orders (TPOs). (See Appendix for legislation and implications)

- hedgerows and individual trees can also be protected where they are within an SSSI, or ASSI in Northern Ireland, national nature reserve, local nature reserve or other protected area

- hedgerows may contain plants which are protected under the **Wildlife and Countryside Act 1981** or the **Wildlife (NI) Order 1985**. It is an offence to intentionally pick, uproot or destroy these plant species without a licence. (See protected plants SBS)

- it is an offence to uproot any wild plant without the landowner's permission. (See protected plants, page 101)

- a number of protected animal species are associated with hedgerows and trees. These include several bat species, which roost in cavities in trees, dormice, badger, reptiles such as adder, grass snake, slow-worm and common lizard plus a wide range of nesting birds.

Protecting hedgerows and trees on site

Hedgerows and trees that are identified for retention will need to be protected. Refer to guidance in Woodland Habitat notes in this site guide.

An example of bad practice – no protection has been put up and the area beneath the tree is being used as a dumping ground for site waste.

Soil

WHAT IS SOIL?

The careful identification and management of soils before and during construction works is essential for the success of any habitat creation, restoration or enhancement scheme! Soil quality can easily be damaged and very expensive to correct.

Surveying soils

Soil surveys may be necessary only on larger projects where a significant amount of soil strip and landscape restoration is planned. Where a soil survey is to be carried out this should be done early in the planning process.

Most construction projects will involve movement of soil. Topsoil in particular is an irreplaceable resource and must be handled appropriately.

Legal protection

There is no legal protection for soil itself, but there may be for the habitats and species that live in or on it. However, in many cases appropriate land restoration is an essential element of the planning permission.

Soil handling and management on site

Plans should include careful consideration of the following:

- soil stripping

- soil storage

- soil re-instatement

- use of appropriate soil moving machinery

- timing of works

- phasing and direction of soil movements

- remedial measures.

Terminology

Topsoil – is the darker, organic surface horizon and is usually 200–300 mm thick.

Subsoil – is the underlying paler soil, but still having an identifiable structure into which plant roots extend for moisture and water. Normally it extends down to 1–1.2 m below the surface.

Overburden – is the mineral parent material of the soil, different from subsoil in that it lacks roots and a soil structure.

Methods for soil movement may vary depending whether soils are moved for engineering purposes or nature conservation purposes.

A very useful checklist for the specific issues to be considered when planning soil handling operations can be found in the publication *Developing Naturally* (Oxford 2000, pp 148 to 149).

Wherever possible avoid storing and double-handling soils; aim to move them straight to any designated receptor sites. This will help conserve their quality as well as proving cheaper.

Soil stripping

Irreversible compaction, smearing and loss of soil structure can be caused by handling and movement of soils in unfavourable weather and soil moisture conditions, by unsuitable storage of soils, and by passage of machinery with high axle weights or ground pressures across soils.

- machine operators should strip and move using methods that ensure that soils are not damaged
- topsoil and subsoil should always be kept separate
- two systems for handling soil are commonly used:
  - earthscrapers
  - dumptruck and excavator (sometimes with hybrids of the two).

The dumptruck method, if correctly implemented, should minimise soil compaction and allow movement of soils across a wider range of moisture contents than a scraper. It may also reduce the need for remedial work during the aftercare period (see *Mineral Planning Guidance MPG 7*: Annex A, Section 34).

Stockpiling

Avoid stockpiling soils where possible. Where essential:

- ensure the stockpile site is prepared and is not in an area that may be waterlogged or affected by flood water
- store topsoil, subsoil and overburden in separate stockpiles

- aeration is critical, especially to topsoil. Air can penetrate into soil approximately one metre, so consider the height and profile of stockpiles carefully – wide and low is the best profile. As a rule of thumb, 3–4 metres high is the maximum for topsoil, 4–5 metres for subsoil

- sowing the soil with grass or leguminous seed mix will help stabilise it, and is also essential for helping to retain the soil in good condition. However, this may not be appropriate for certain types of habitats

- do not allow the stockpile to get too wet.

Note that stockpiling will slowly result in soil degradation and *should be restricted to the minimum time necessary*. Most soils will suffer some deterioration in less than a year, others more quickly.

Soil reinstatement

The soils will go back in reverse order, overburden first, followed by subsoil and finally topsoil. It is important that machines do not travel over the soils. Some ripping of subsoil, or even topsoil may be necessary to relieve compaction, and to enhance drainage and growing conditions.

Soil and habitats

When translocating habitats it is essential to consider the soil requirements in terms of movement, storage and issues such as aspect, slope and drainage.

Remember topsoil contains the very valuable seed bank – usually within the top 15 cm of the soil. Mishandling of topsoil can jeopardise the success of habitat creation or translocation.

In creating some wildlife habitat, the use of subsoil as a growing medium may be preferred to that of topsoil. This is taken to its extreme in the creation of new wasteland sites or brown roofs where materials such as crushed brick and concrete alone are used.

Timing of works

Preferably work with soils in dry conditions, and never when it is raining or shortly after rain, or when soils are waterlogged or frozen.

Avoid stripping and re-spreading soils in winter. *Soil should never be stripped from land when it is wetter than the plastic limit.*

A simple way of determining whether or not soil is in the right condition to move is to get a pre-moulded ball of soil and roll it on a piece of glass.

The plastic limit of soil is reached when it just fails to roll into a 3 mm diameter thread. If you are able to roll it narrower than this then it is too wet and the soil should not be moved.

Useful references:

- *BS 3882:1994 Specification for topsoil. BSI.*

- *Mineral Planning Guidance No 7: The Reclamation of Mineral Workings. Sections A29 to A58 of Annex A (HMSO, London).*

Urban habitats

WHAT ARE URBAN HABITATS?

Urban habitats include parks and open spaces, allotments, private gardens, and areas of vacant or brownfield land.

Characteristics of brownfield habitats

Many sites have a mix of different soils and substrates. These typically include demolition products such as crushed brick and concrete, as well sand and clay. Some of the most distinctive brownfield sites are former industrial waste tips and contain materials such as PFA, alkali-waste or lime-kiln dust.

Complex patterns of vegetation is one of the reasons why brownfield sites are so rich in biodiversity.

Why protect them?

Recent years have seen increasing pressure on the brownfield resource as Government policies favour redevelopment on brownfield, as opposed to greenfield land. As a result the amount of brownfield land is probably at its lowest for a number of decades.

Legal protection

Some urban habitats are protected by designation, eg:

- SSSI

- ASSI(NI)

- NNR

- LNR

- SAC

- SPA

- SINC

- SLNC(NI).

Butterfly bush growing on an urban wasteland site in London

Some plants found in urban habitats receive legal protection which makes it an offence to intentionally pick, uproot or destroy any of these plants without a licence.

The black redstart is a rare bird species that occupies brownfield sites with abandoned buildings or other built structures

- these specially protected plants are all rare but they can turn up in new and unexpected locations. It is also an offence for uproot any wild plant without the landowner's permission. Refer to protected plant SBS for details

- a number of protected animal species are also associated with urban habitats, for example common lizard and slow-worm

- great crested newts frequently occur in urban ponds, and water voles may occur along urban rivers and other watercourses

- urban areas are especially important for certain bird species that are in decline, including house sparrows, starlings, swifts, the black redstart and peregrine falcon

- bats commonly roost in buildings, including modern houses.

The pipistrelle bat is one of the bat species often encountered in urban areas

Protecting urban habitats on site

- Any areas of habitat that are of special conservation value should be identified and protected. This will usually involve the erection of some form of protective fencing such as chestnut paling mounted on a scaffold framework. Signs should be erected stating that the area is protected and that there is no access for site vehicles or staff without the permission of the environment manager.

- Some urban habitats – such as those commonly found on brownfield land – are relatively robust and potentially capable of coping with a certain amount of disturbance. For example, it may be possible to provide temporary access across an area of brownfield habitat without causing irreparable damage. Nevertheless, such habitats are potentially vulnerable to a range of direct and indirect construction impacts. Changes in hydrology (eg through drainage or flooding of an area) can significantly alter the character of the vegetation. The accumulation of silt from run-off is also potentially damaging, as is dust.

Urban sites are likely to feature invasive plants such as Japanese knotweed. See invasive species briefing

- Urban habitats are also likely to feature invasive plants such as Japanese knotweed and giant hogweed.

- Translocation and recreation of brownfield habitat is increasingly being looked at as a possible mitigation measure where protected species are affected by development (eg green or "brown" roofs to provide substitute habitat for black redstarts).

Wetland

TYPES OF WETLAND?

Wetlands include rivers, streams, dykes, ditches, ponds, lakes, marshes, swamps, reedbeds and bogs and saltmarsh. (See coastal/marine SBS).

Wetlands can be either permanent or temporary (seasonal) and can be fed by either surface water or groundwater.

Conservation status

Wetlands have declined greatly as a result of drainage, reclamation for agriculture and development. Those wetlands that survive are often degraded through pollution or drainage.

A small lake – or large pond!

Legal protection

Valuable wetlands receive protection through a site designation such as:

- SSSI
- ASSI(NI)
- NNR
- LNR
- RAMSAR
- SPA
- SAC/cSAC
- SINC

Ditches such as the one above are important strongholds of the watervole

Other protective designations include groundwater protection zones or waters designated under the EC Fisheries Directive.

A number of wetland plants receive legal protection which makes it an offence to intentionally pick, uproot or destroy them without a licence.

- it is an offence to uproot any wild plant without the landowner's permission

- refer to protected plants SBS

- a number of protected animal species are associated with wetland habitats. These include otter, water vole, great crested newt, grass snake, a wide range of nesting birds, fish such as brook lamprey and bullhead, white-clawed crayfish and some other invertebrates

- note that the Water Framework Directive is likely to influence the design and implementation of construction projects that affect inland and coastal waters.

Protecting wetland on site:

- don't forget that any works involving water and wetlands may require a consent from the Environment Agency, SEPA or NI-EHS

- wetland areas of special conservation importance should be identified and protected. This will usually involve the erection of some form of protective fencing such as chestnut paling mounted on a scaffold framework. Signs should be erected stating that the area is protected and that there is no access for site vehicles or staff without the permission of the environment manager

- it is advisable to retain a buffer strip around the margins of any protected wetland areas, to intercept silt carried in run-off before it enters the wetland and to protect from other forms of pollution

- wetland habitats are very sensitive to changes in hydrology. Drainage or changes in flow into and out of the wetland can cause irreparable damage and may jeopardise its survival

- wetland habitats are also very susceptible to compaction and in general it is advisable to keep machinery out of wetland areas. Where crossing a wetland is unavoidable, try to use low ground pressure machinery and utilise geotextile mats or sleeper mattresses

- a number of protected species are associated with the various types of wetland habitat. Appropriate surveys should be conducted early in the project to ensure that any impacts on them can be minimised.

Other factors that could cause damage to wetlands include the following:

- *all forms of pollution*, incl. silt and dust.

- *changes in water chemistry*, for example alkaline water entering acid water habitats and vice versa – care should be taken with choice of materials for haul roads etc (for instance avoid limestone in acid areas), and when pumping ground water into surface waters. Concrete washout pits should be located carefully.

- *disturbance*, noise or physical presence of people or machinery, eg otter or ground-nesting birds.

Woodland and scrub

TYPES OF WOODLAND

Ancient woodland
The only woods that are likely to have a link with the distant past are those that are called "ancient woodland". These are woods that, from documentary evidence, we know existed before 1600 and so are more likely to have a link with the original forest.

Secondary woodland
Most other woodland is termed "recent" or "secondary" woodland. This occupies land that has not had continuous woodland cover since 1600 – in other words, at some time over the last four centuries, it has been open land that has either subsequently been replanted or has naturally regenerated into woodland.

Plantations
Virtually all coniferous forest or woodland in Britain is planted. In the 20th century large areas were planted as single species plantations, principally for timber production. Broadleaf plantations can also be found.

Other forms of woodland
In the highlands of Scotland coniferous evergreen forest survives – the so-called Caledonian pine forest. There are also some small areas of juniper woodland in upland parts of England and Scotland, and yew woodland on the chalk in southern England.

Scrub

Scrub is defined as vegetation dominated by shrubs, usually less than five metres in height, eg hawthorn, blackthorn, bramble, elder and gorse.

It is an extremely valuable habitat for wildlife particularly as part of a mosaic with other habitats such as woodland, grassland and wetland. Birds, reptiles, amphibians and mammals can all benefit.

An area of scrub on the edge of grassland habitat

Legal protection

Woods can receive protection through **tree preservation orders** (TPOs) and/or through designation as the following:

- you are not allowed to fell a woodland or remove more than a few trees without obtaining a felling licence from the Forestry Authority

- ancient woodlands protection is being considered.

- SSSI
- ASSI(NI)
- SAC
- LNR
- NNR
- SINC

See Appendix.

A number of woodland plants receive legal protection which makes it an offence to intentionally pick, uproot or destroy any of these plants without a licence.

It is an offence to uproot any wild plant without the landowners' permission. Refer to protected plants species briefing sheets that form the woodland or scrub.

Many protected animal species are also associated with woodland habitats, for example dormouse, red squirrel, badger, pine marten and some bat species. See relevant SPS notes.

Protecting woodland and scrub on site

Any woodland or scrub that is not to be cleared should be fenced off with chestnut paling fencing mounted on a scaffold framework. BS 5837:1991 – *Trees in Relation to Construction* provides guidance on tree protection. The main points are:

- fencing should be strong and durable. In most cases it should be at least 1.2 m high, comprising a vertical and horizontal framework of scaffolding braced to resist impacts, supporting either chestnut paling or chain link. In some situations more substantial fencing, consisting of 2.4 m high exterior grade ply or similar boarding may be necessary

- protect as large an area around the tree(s) as possible. Minimum distances to be protected are defined in BS 5837, but as a rule the fencing should be placed no closer than the outermost limit of branch spread or at a distance equal to half of the tree height, whichever is the greater

- signs should be erected stating that the fenced area is protected and that there is no access for site vehicles or staff without the permission of the environment manager, or similar words. No materials should be stored in the protected areas

- tree roots are particularly susceptible to damage and, because they are not visible, are frequently ignored. Most roots lie within the top 600 mm of soil and they may extend beyond the spread of the crown.

Damage to roots can occur through:

- soil compaction
- raising of soil levels over the root system.
- flooding.
- covering the rooting area with materials (such as concrete or tarmac).
- pollution and spillages.
- direct physical damage as a result of excavations and topsoil stripping
- material storage.

Appendix

Summary of wildlife legislation, planning and guidance relevant to the construction industry in the UK.

(For detailed information on individual species, refer to pages 30–41)

This summary does not provide the definitive word on all legislation and guidance that are current in the UK; it merely attempts to provide a summary of the relevant key points for those involved in the construction industry.

For further information the following provide useful reference material, or otherwise consult the primary legislation or guidance itself.

- *Urban Environments and Wildlife Laws* (Rees 2002)

- *Developing Naturally* (Oxford 2000)

- www.defra.gov.uk/paw
  www.odem.gov.uk
  www.scotland.gov.uk
  www.wales.gov.uk
  www.ehsni.gov.uk
  www.rtpi.org.uk

Legislation/Planning Guidance	Where does it apply?	Effect	What it means for you	Other information
A) Relevant planning legislation				
Town & Country Planning Act 1990 (as amended)	E & W	Places a duty on LPAs to make adequate provision for trees when planning permission is granted.	Know whether or not your project is covered by a Tree Preservation Order, or is located within a designated conservation area.	There are exemptions to this, for example if the tree is dangerous, or if the LPA has consented to any otherwise prohibited operations.
Town & Country Planning (Trees) Regulations 1999 (SI 1999/1892)	E & W	It protects existing trees under a Tree Preservation Order (TPO) and allows LPAs to require that new trees	Do not cut, lop, uproot, damage, or destroy trees or woodland that are protected by a TPO.	Trees can only be felled after obtaining a licence from the Forest Authority. This does not apply to:
Planning (Tree Preservation Order) Regulations 1973	NI	may be planted and that once planted are then covered by a TPO. Trees in designated conservation areas (ie building conservation areas) are subject to statutory restrictions.	Follow guidelines for protecting trees on construction sites contained in British Standard BS5837: 1991 – *Guide for trees in relation to construction.*	– trees in gardens, orchards, churchyards or public open spaces – fruit trees – dead or diseased trees – trees of 8 cm or less in diameter measured at 1.3 m above ground – thinnings with a diameter of 10 cm or less, or coppice or underwood with a diameter of 15 cm or less.
		LPAs may protect trees by making a Tree Protection Order (TPO). A TPO can be used to protect – a single tree – a group of trees		
Town & Country Planning (Scotland) Act 1997	S	– an entire woodland.		
Planning (NI) Order (1997)	NI			In Northern Ireland LPA duties are carried out by the Department of the Environment Planning Service
The planning and Compensation Act 1991	E & W	Deals with contravention of the planning laws and the enforcement of planning conditions	Ensure that you abide by planning law and any planning conditions that may have been set for your project	Some LPAs interpret this Act as providing justification for seeking a net gain for biodiversity from a development proposal
Hedgerow Regulations 1997 (SI 1997/1160)	E & W	Gives LPAs the powers to prevent the removal of "important" hedgerows. Makes it illegal to remove most countryside hedgerows without permission of the LPA.	Ensure that you submit a Hedgerow Removal Notice to the LPA before removing any section of a hedgerow that is more than 20 metres long. This is not required if removal is in implementation of a planning permission. Make sure that you are aware of any "important" hedgerows on your site and take steps to protect them.	The definition of hedgerow is set out in the regulations. It includes hedges that have existed for at least 30 years and are of archeological and historical importance or of wildlife and landscape importance. If the hedgerow is important and you are refused permission to remove it, the LPA must serve a Hedgerow Retention Notice.

Legislation/Planning Guidance	Where does it apply?	Effect	What it means for you	Other information
B) Relevant EIA Regulations and circulars				
Town & Country Planning (Environmental Impact Assessment) (England and Wales) Regulations 1999	E & W	Requires that environmental impact assessment (EIA) be carried out for certain types of project that are likely to have significant environmental effects.	Consider carefully whether or not your project will require an EIA under the provision of the regulations. Even if it does not, ensure that you carry out ecological screening studies to find out if an ecological assessment is needed.	Amended in 2000 to apply to mineral planning authorities. **There are also other regulations covering the assessment of particular kinds of construction or other activity such as forestry, harbours, pipelines, water resources, uncultivated land and semi-natural areas (search www.hmso.gov.uk for a full list).**
Environmental Impact Assessment (Scotland) Regulations 1999 (SSI 1999/1)	S	(as above)	(as above)	Forestry operations and fish farming included under a separate but similar Regulation
Planning (Environmental Impact Assessment) Regulations (NI) 1999 (SR 1999/73)	NI	(as above)	(as above)	Forestry operations and roads included under a separate but similar Regulation
Circulars 13/1999 and 6/1995 (Scotland)	E/S	Sets out expectations of when an EIA will be needed	If you are a planner or designer you should be aware of the guidance given on wildlife in Circulars 13/1991 and 6/1995 and other planning documents.	
Technical Advice (Wales) Note 5, Nature conservation and Planning, November 1996	W	Also sets out explanations of when an EIA will be needed	If you are a planner or designer you should be aware of the guidance given on wildlife in various Welsh and UK-wide planning documents.	

Legislation/Planning Guidance	Where does it apply?	Effect	What it means for you	Other information
C) Key wildlife legislation				
Wildlife & Countryside Act 1981 (as amended) (WCA)	E & W & S	Affords protection to all birds, their nests and eggs. Makes it illegal to kill, injure or take any wild bird and take, damage or destroy their nest or eggs. For bird species listed in Schedule 1 it is also illegal, for example, to disturb them when they are nesting.	Do not carry out site clearance when birds are nesting, ie March to August but some species will nest outside of these times. If in doubt check for nesting birds before felling trees, demolishing buildings and structures or clearing scrub. For Schedule 1 birds, even if the nest is not to be destroyed, a licence may be needed because it is an offence to disturb Schedule 1 birds whilst they are nesting. Advice must be formally sought from Defra (E&W) or SEERAD (S) to clarify whether a licence is needed. It is recommended that surveys are carried out to determine what species are present on site before development works start.	It is possible to get a licence (from Defra or SEERAD) to undertake works that would normally be deemed illegal under the WCA. General licences are available for certain named species, such as feral pigeons and members of the crow family, to preserve public health, public safety or air safety, or to conserve wild birds. It is also possible to apply for individual licences from Defra/ SEERAD for other species and purposes given in Section 16 of the 1981 Act It is a defence against prosecution under the WCA that a potentially illegal act was the incidental result of an otherwise lawful operation and could not be "reasonably" avoided. Undertaking a survey and proposing appropriate mitigation may be considered as having taken reasonable steps to avoid an offence taking place. However, only the courts can decide on what is reasonable.
		Protects certain animals such as bats, badgers, great crested newts, slow worms, lizards and/or the places and structures they use for shelter and protection. The degree of protection depends on the species. The provisions also include some marine animals, including dolphins, whales and basking sharks, some species of fish and some invertebrates.	Make sure you know if any protected species are on your site. If necessary, carry out relevant surveys and do so at the right time of year. If protected species are on site, either ensure that they are protected during the construction phase or that they are moved out of harm's way. Note that licences may be necessary to carry out these activities – ensure that there is sufficient time in your programme to acquire licences and to plan mitigation before any works begin.	A few species of plant also receive protection. It is illegal to uproot or destroy any wild plant if you are not an authorised person, ie owner or occupier of land or authorised by such persons. It may be necessary to consult the statutory nature conservation organisations (SNCOs). A licence may be needed either from the SNCO or from Defra/SEERAD to undertake certain activities.

Legislation/ Planning Guidance	Where does it apply?	Effect	What it means for you	Other information
Wildlife & Countryside Act 1981 (as amended) (WCA) cont.	E & W & S	Enables the designation and protection of land as a Site of Special Scientific Interest (SSSI).	Keep well clear of SSSIs! These are the best wildlife sites in the country and may comprise sites of European or international importance. They are high profile and well protected by the law and by planning guidance (see also *CRoW Act*). If you are developing a site near an SSSI try to leave an adequate buffer strip between your development and the boundary of the SSSI, and make sure that there are no indirect impacts on the interest of it.	Protection of SSSIs has been strengthened under the *CRoW Act 2000* (*E&W*). Consent is needed from an SNCO for works that may have a damaging effect on an SSSI.
		Makes it illegal to release or allow to escape into the wild certain animals.

Makes it illegal to plant or otherwise 'introduce into the wild' Japanese knotweed, giant hogweed or giant kelp. | Japanese knotweed and, to a lesser extent, giant hogweed can be a major problem for the construction industry. In effect these plants are so easy to "introduce into the wild" that breaking the law is a distinct possibility. The trouble is that they are very difficult to get rid of – in the case of Japanese knotweed it can take three years or more to eradicate the plant. What is more it can be very expensive. | Make sure you know whether, and if so where, these plants are on your site, and take advice from an ecologist on how to control them. |
| | | Enables the establishment of Marine Nature Reserves (MNRs). | Avoid working in MNRs. Construction works can do a great deal of damage to marine habitats and secondary impacts such as an increase in localised pollution can be equally destructive. | To date three MNRs have been designated.
• Lundy, Bristol Channel
• Skomer, Dyfed
• Strangford Lough, Northern Ireland. |
| **Wildlife (Northern Ireland) Order 1985 and Amendment (1995)** | NI | Provides corresponding protection to wild birds and a range of other species (eg common lizard, otter, badgers) in Northern Ireland as WCA 1981 does in England, Wales and Scotland.

In addition, all birds are protected on Sundays. | See guidance under WCA | Amended by **Wildlife Order 1995.** Pest species can be controlled under terms of general licences issued by the Environment and Heritage Service. |

Legislation/ Planning Guidance	Where does it apply?	Effect	What it means for you	Other information
Environment (NI) Order 2002	NI	The NI equivalent to an SSSI designation is an Area of Special Scientific Interest (ASSI).	Consent is needed from EHS-NH for works that may have a damaging effect on an ASSI (see guidance under WCA).	
Nature Conservation (Scotland) Act 2004	S	Provides for increased protection for SSSIs in Scotland and provides for enhanced species protection by covering offences including "recklessness".	Greater care needed when protected species may be present or when working near SSIs.	
Weeds Act 1959	E, W & S	The Weeds Act is concerned with the control of what are called injurious weeds and preventing their spread onto adjacent land. The Act covers five species of injurious weed all of which are native species commonly found through the UK. These are: • Spear thistle • Creeping thistle • Curled dock • Broad-leafed dock • Common ragwort	Be aware that you may be called upon to control these weeds if you occupy any land on which they are growing. Do not take action against these plants unless you need to and are 100% sure that they are what you think they are. There are plants that are closely related to these species and look very similar, but are much rarer and are not injurious weeds.	Defra or SEERAD can serve notice on the occupier of land to take action to remove the weeds.
Noxious Weeds (NI) Order 1977	NI	(as above)	(as above)	DARD can serve notice on the occupier of land to take action to remove the weeds.

Legislation/Planning Guidance	Where does it apply?	Effect	What it means for you	Other information
Conservation (Natural Habitats etc) Regulations 1994 amended in S & W by the *Conservation (Natural Habitats etc) (Amendment) 1997* and in England by the *Conservation (Natural Habitats etc) (Amendment) (England) Regulations 2000* referred to as *Habitats Regulations 1994* throughout this document.	E & W & S	Important sites are designated Special Areas of Conservation (SAC) and are also referred to, along with Special Protection Areas (SPAs) as "European Sites" – in the UK these are generally legally protected in the form of SSSIs, but receive greater protection as European sites. Amends the WCA 1981 to bring it in line with the *Habitats Directive 92/43* giving greater protection (under schedule 2) to a variety of native animals including bats, dormice, great crested newt, otters and the large blue butterfly (European Protected Species). Schedule 4 also identifies European protected plants.	When considering a site, ensure that surveys are carried out at the earliest possible opportunity to determine whether European protected species are present. The presence of such species must be included for consideration as part of any planning application made to a planning authority. It is an offence to deliberately kill, injure, take or disturb animal species listed in Schedule 2 of the regulations, to destroy their resting places or breeding sites; or to pick, collect, cut, uproot or otherwise destroy plant species listed in Schedule 4. Animals listed in Schedule 3 of the regulations may be taken or killed only in certain ways. Licences to undertake works regarding European protected species are obtained from Defra or SEERAD, and must satisfy three criteria: • the works must be for reasons of preserving public health or safety, or of other over-riding public interest • there is no satisfactory alternative • actions will not be detrimental to favourable conservation status of the species.	Note that the English Government intend to include provisions for European protected species as contained within the *Habitats Directive* within the land use planning regime in the near future.
Conservation (Natural Habitats etc) Regulations (NI) 1995 and Amendments 1997	NI	See guidance for E, W & S above	See guidance for E, W & S above	

Legislation/Planning Guidance	Where does it apply?	Effect	What it means for you	Other information
Countryside and Rights of Way Acts 2000 (CRoW Act)	E & W	The *CRoW Act* gives the UK Biodiversity Action Plan a statutory basis. It enables courts to order the restoration of an SSSI where a person or a public body has been convicted of damaging or destroying it. It provides SNCOs with powers to refuse consent for damaging operations and to encourage active management of the land.	Any work carried out for a government department may require special measures to be undertaken in accord with national and local biodiversity action plans. Do not damage or destroy a SSSI unless you have the necessary permissions. In fact, avoid going anywhere near one if possible. If any impacts on an SSSI from your development are predicted, ensure that all consents and agreements to proceed are in place in sufficient time.	Lists of important species and habitats are available at www.ukbap.org.uk This does not apply in Scotland, as SSSIs are now a devolved matter. The new S.28G imposes a duty on "public bodies" (defined as ministers, government departments, local authorities, statutory undertakers (public or private) and other public bodies) in exercising their functions to take reasonable steps to further conservation and enhancement of the special features on an SSSI or on adjacent land.
		Strengthens legal protection for threatened species and updates the WCA 1981. Introduces into the WCA 1981 the new offence of "recklessly disturbing" Schedule 1 birds and the sheltering places of certain Schedule 5 animals. Enables courts to impose heavier fines and prison sentences for all wildlife offences (generally up to £5000 and/or six months imprisonment per offence – ie per animal).	Make sure that you know whether or not you have protected species on site. In particular, check carefully for animals such as bats, which you might not think are about, but are so small that only an expert is likely to see or find them.	Schedule 5 of the WCA includes all bats, great crested newts and a variety of insects and other animals.
Water Resources Act 1991	E & W	Makes it an offence to cause, or knowingly permit pollution of controlled waters.	For example, silt from run-off can have a devastating effect on the ecology of a river.	Controlled waters include rivers, streams, canals, groundwaters, coastal waters and territorial waters. Lakes and ponds are not usually covered by the definition unless they drain into other controlled waters.
Salmon and Freshwater Fisheries Act 1975	E & W	Makes it illegal to put anything into waters containing fish (or tributaries of such waters) that may poison or injure fish, their spawn, spawning grounds or food of such fish. S10 requires a licence from the EA or SEPA to introduce fish or spawn into an inland waterway.	Do not pollute waters of any kind, and take care in particular regarding site run-off. If carrying out fish translocation as part of, for example, a stream diversion, check with the EA, SEPA or EHS-EP to see if you require a licence.	
Foyle Fisheries Act 1952 and Fisheries Act 1966	NI			
Salmon and Freshwater Fisheries (Consolidation Scotland) Act 2003	S			

Legislation/Planning Guidance	Where does it apply?	Effect	What it means for you	Other information
Deer Act 1991 *Wildlife (Northern Ireland) Order 1985* *Deer (Scotland) Act 1996*	E & W NI S	Regulates killing and taking of deer	Apart from not intentionally killing, taking or injuring deer on site, also take steps to prevent deer from being killed or harmed by your development. For example, on a road project, deer fencing may be necessary.	
Protection of Badgers Act 1992	E & W	Makes it illegal to wilfully kill, injure or take a badger, or indeed to be in possession of a live or dead badger. It is also illegal to damage, destroy or obstruct access to a badger sett, cause a dog to enter a badger sett or to disturb a badger when it is occupying a set.	Make sure that you know where any badger setts are near your site. If you are working near a badger sett you may need a licence. In no way interfere with any holes in the ground without having them checked by an ecologist first. Badger setts are not always obviously different from rabbit holes or fox earths. In exceptional circumstances, if you need to move a badger sett, you must get a licence before you do it. It is possible for a badger to establish a sett in the middle of a construction site after work has started!	Only the issues covering construction are dealt with here. The Protection of Badgers Act is principally designed to prevent badger digging and baiting, and thus includes other actions that are deemed illegal. Consult the Act if you need to know more about these.
Protection of Animals Act 1911	E & W	Prevents cruel treatment of captive animals or causing unnecessary suffering during transport.	If you need to keep an animal captive, ensure you care for its welfare and cause no suffering. In such cases consult your ecologist, the SNCO or the RSPCA as soon as possible.	Captive includes situations where an animal is prevented from escaping by being constrained in a small place, for example during excavation of burrows.
Protection of Animals (Scotland) Act 1960	S	(as above)	(as above)	(as above)
Abandonment of Animals Act 1960	E & W & S	Makes it illegal to leave species (including wild animals) for any length of time or to reintroduce them into the wild inappropriately after having held them captive.	If you need to keep an animal captive, ensure you do not abandon it. Do not introduce back into the wild without sufficient planning, supervision and if necessary licensing.	

Legislation/Planning Guidance	Where does it apply?	Effect	What it means for you	Other information
Welfare of Animals Act (NI) 1972	NI	Prohibits cruelty to animals. Applies to all animals including wild animals.	(as for *Protection of Animals Act 1911* and *Abandonment of Animals Act 1960*)	
Wild Mammals (Protection) Act 1966	E & W & S	Makes it illegal to treat cruelly wild mammals, including crushing, drowning, asphyxiating etc.	Do your best to ensure that, as far as is possible, any wild mammals will not be harmed by site clearance operations. This includes rabbits, squirrels, hedgehogs etc.	
The Convention on Wetlands of International Importance especially as Waterfowl habitat 1971 (Ramsar Convention)	All signatory countries including UK	Requires signatory states to designate important wetlands for special protection (Ramsar sites). Ramsar sites are protected as SSSIs in Britain and as ASSIs in Northern Ireland.	Avoid development of designated sites. If your site is near a designated site allow sufficient buffer zones and take extra care.	There are 144 Ramsar sites in the UK.
The Bonn Convention on the Conservation of Migratory Species of Wild Animals 1979	All signatory countries including UK	Applied in the UK by the WCA 1981	Know which species enjoy special protection. Make sure that you know what species are on or near your site.	
The Berne Convention on the Conservation of European Wildlife and Natural Habitats 1979	All signatory countries including UK	Includes the introduction of Biogenic Reserves designated by the council of Europe for heathlands and grasslands.

Encourages the re-introduction of native species as a method of conservation. | Find out whether there are any special introduction programmes for birds and other forms of wildlife in the area in which you are planning your development, ie natterjack toad, sand lizard. | |

Legislation/Planning Guidance	Where does it apply?	Effect	What it means for you	Other information
Wild Birds Directive (Directive 79/409/EEC) Also know as the **Birds Directive**	E & W & S & NI	This Directive enabled the establishment of Special Protection Areas (SPAs) that are legally protected in GB as SSSIs and in Northern Ireland as ASSIs.	SPAs, together with SACs make up the "Natura 2000" Network of European Protected Sites. SPAs are the best sites for birds in the UK and development that might affect them should be avoided.	There are 87 SPAs in England alone, covering approximately 597 000 ha. Further information can be obtained from the JNCC website at www.jncc.gov.uk
Water Framework Directive (Directive 2000/60/EC) (WFD)	E & W & S & NI	Requires all inland and coastal waters to reach "good status" by 2015. It will do this by establishing a river basin district structure within which demanding environmental objectives will be set, including ecological targets for surface waters. The purpose of the directive is, among other things, to: ● prevent further deterioration and protect and enhance aquatic ecosystems ● ensure the progressive reduction of pollution of groundwater ● provide definitions of ecological classifications for water environments as High, Good or Moderate status. With regard to potential pollutants the WFD introduces categories of "priority substances" that will need to be removed from discharges.	Basically the directive is seeking higher standards of water protection with the aim of achieving improved water quality as measured in biological and chemical terms. Improved quality of discharge to controlled waters is likely to be one of the implications for the construction industry. Another is more work upgrading sewage treatment works!	In the future soft engineering solutions e.g. creating meanders and restoring flood plains, are more likely to be favoured than hard engineered solutions as they put habitats back rather than destroying them. Implementation of the WFD will largely fall to the EA, SEPA and EHS (NI).

Useful organisations

General

Association of Local Government Ecologists (ALGE)
www.alge.org.uk

Biological Records Centre
www.brc.ac.uk

British Library Environmental Information Service
www.bl.uk

Centre for Environmental Data and Recording (CEDaR)
www.habitats.org.uk/cedar

The Countryside Agency
www.countryside.gov.uk

Countryside Council for Wales
www.ccw.gov.uk

Defra European Wildlife Division
www.defra.gov.uk

Department of the Environment for Northern Ireland
www.doeni.gov.uk

Department for Transport
www.dft.gov.uk

English Nature
www.english-nature.org.uk

Environment Agency
www.environment-agency.gov.uk

**Environment and Heritage Service of Northern Ireland
Environmental Protection**
www.ehsni.gov.uk

**Environment and Heritage Service of Northern Ireland
Natural Heritage**
www.ehsni.gov.uk

Institute of Ecology and Environmental Management
www.ieem.org.uk

Institute of Environmental Management and Assessment (IEMA)
www.iema.net

Joint Nature Conservation Committee (JNCC)
www.jncc.gov.uk

National Biodiversity Network
www.nbn.org.uk

The National Trust
www.nationaltrust.org.uk

Natural Environment Research Council
www.nerc.ac.uk

Office of the Deputy Prime Minister
www.odpm.gov.uk

Royal Society for Prevention of Cruelty to Animals (RSPCA)
www.rspca.org.uk

Scottish Environment Protection Agency
www.sepa.org.uk

Scottish Executive Environment and Rural Affairs Department
www.scotland.gov.uk/who/dept_rural.asp

Scottish Natural Heritage
www.snh.org.uk

Wildfowl and Wetlands Trust
www.wwt.org.uk

Wildlife Trusts
www.wildlifetrusts.org

WorldWide Fund for Nature
www.wwf-uk.org

Plants

Arboricultural Association
www.trees.org.uk

British Bryological Society
www.britishbryologicalsociety.org.uk

Flora

Botanical Society of the British Isles
www.bsbi.org.uk

Flora Locale
www.floralocale.org

Forestry Commission (inc Forest Enterprise, Forestry Research)
www.forestry.gov.uk

Forest Service (Northern Ireland)
www.forestserviceni.gov.uk

National Wildflower Centre
www.nwc.org.uk

Plantlife
www.plantlife.org.uk

Woodland Trust
www.woodland-trust.org.uk

Landscape design, sustainable buildings and environmental business

Building for Nature Project
www.seeda.co.uk

Environmental Practice at Work
www.epaw.co.uk

The Landscape Institute
www.l-i.org.uk

Habitats and habitat management

British Waterways
www.british-waterways.org

Centre for Ecology and Hydrology
www.ceh.ac.uk

Chartered Institute of Water and Environmental Management
www.ciwem.org.uk

Marine Conservation Society
www.mcsuk.org

Wildfowl and Wetlands Trust
www.wwt.org.uk

Archaeology and historic heritage

British Geological Society
www.bgs.ac.uk

Council for British Archaeology
www.britarch.ac.uk

English Heritage
www.english-heritage.org.uk

Environment & Heritage Service of Northern Ireland
Build Heritage
www.ehsni.gov.uk

Historic Scotland
www.historic-scotland.gov.uk

Institute of Field Archaeologists
www.archaeologists.net

Species advice

Barn Owl Trust
www.barnowltrust.org.uk

Bat Conservation Trust
www.bats.org.uk

BirdLife International
www.birdlife.net

British Hertpetological Society
www.thebhs.org

British Ornithologists' Union
www.bou.org.uk

British Trust for Ornithology
www.bto.org

Butterfly Conservation
www.butterfly-conservation.org

Froglife
www.froglife.org

The Game Conservancy Trust
www.gct.org.uk

Hawk and Owl Trust
www.hawkandowl.org

Herpetological Conservation Trust
www.herpconstrust.org.uk

Mammal Society
www.abdn.ac.uk/mammal

National Federation of Badger Groups
www.badgers.org.uk

The Northern Ireland Bat Group

www.batsni.org.uk

Otter Trust

www.ottertrust.org.uk

Royal Society for the Protection of Birds (RSPB)

www.rspb.org.uk